# indian takeaway

## One boy's take on three continents

**Bharat Patel**

All profits from the sale of this book go to
Hope Against Cancer,
Leicestershire and Rutland's cancer charity.

The opinions expressed have no connection with Hope.

Indian Takeaway
ISBN: 978-1-910181-71-3
Published September 2019

Printed and Published by Anchorprint Group Limited
www.anchorprint.co.uk

To Andy, Natalie, Alex, Ba
and all my family

# Acknowledgements

My thanks to Peter Kitchen for the illustrations and cover image,
to photographer Nick Roberts, to Anchorprint for help with artwork
and printing costs and to Tank PR for marketing advice.
Also to John Florance for his suggestions and corrections and most of all
to Andy, for using her superhuman powers of shortening,
sharpening and burnishing.

# Contents

# Principal characters

Bhulima – my paternal grandmother

*Ba* – my mother

*Bapuji* –my father

*Nana* – my paternal uncle

*Nani* – my aunt, *Nana*'s wife

Kumud – my sister

*Foy* – my paternal aunt

*Fouaji* – *Foy*'s husband

Ramanfouaji – *Fouaji*'s younger brother

Gangama – my maternal grandmother

Kishormama – my maternal uncle

# Preface

Much of this is true, but not all of it. How much even I cannot say because the memory plays tricks. What follows is the story of my odd and eventful journey from India to Africa and then on to England plus intermittent flights of imagination. Some places are real and others are not, so a map would be of limited use. All the characters exist or existed in some form, but many are amalgams of different people and some, but not all, of their names have been changed.

The time frame is blurred because events have been moved to make the story flow. I have tried to create not a history but an impression of a bygone era as seen through the eyes of a small boy. Parts of it will seem alien, almost unbelievable, to those who were not there.

India, Africa and Britain are changing fast and the world of this book no longer exists. Some may be shocked by the occasionally outrageous views that are expressed. To paraphrase Charles Dickens, it was the strangest of times, it was the most interesting of times, if not the fairest and best. I'm glad I didn't miss it and it's important never to forget it.

*Bharat Patel 2019*

# first course

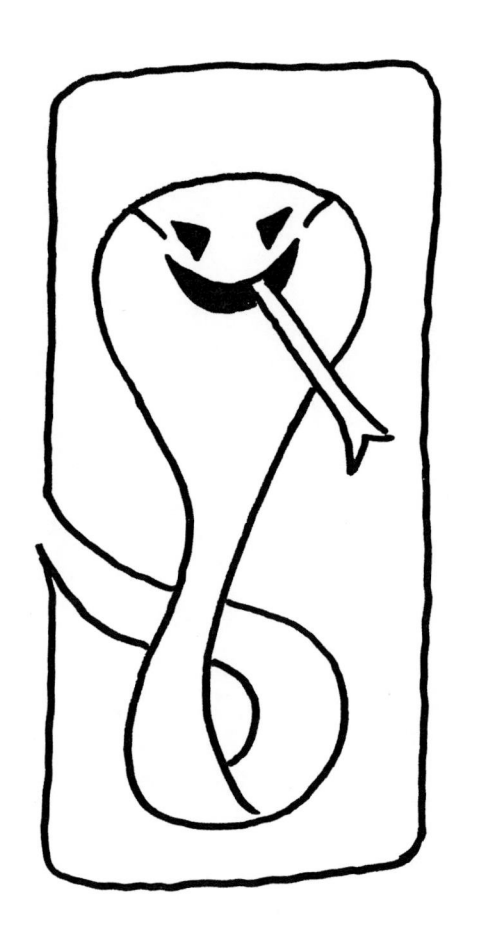

# Chapter 1
## The return of the snakes

**I**nitially our route was only mildly hazardous but it became gradually more menacing and traumatic. We were driving through the deepening darkness from Mumbai Airport at speeds the ancient creaking Ambassador taxi should not have been able to achieve. All three of us were desperate for sleep after a long uncomfortable journey from London but kept awake by the constant honking of horns and a succession of narrow escapes as lorries, bullocks, carts and occasionally camels and wild boars materialised, seemingly out of nowhere.

The animals appeared like ghosts, initially as eyes suspended in mid-air, blinking and glinting in the gloom, then coming into sharp focus, grunting and bellowing and fleeing in terror as we swerved to avoid them. We overtook a slow-moving truck carrying huge overhanging logs by driving to the wrong side of a dual carriageway and only just made it back amid a cacophony of klaxons and shouting.

I was terrified but *Bapuji* and *Ba* had seen it all before. They were unperturbed and the driver did not appear to be deranged, apart from the permanent smile on his face. I fervently wished we had seatbelts; instead we had *Rama*. His statuette sanguinely watched over us from the dashboard, a garish garland of fresh flowers hanging from his neck to his feet. It swung wildly like an out-of control pendulum each time we hit a pothole or swerved too fast round a bend. Miraculously the petals stayed attached.

In Maharashtra the skies were clear and the stars twinkled and I soon spotted the Plough and then the Pole Star. I'd travelled almost five thousand miles and, exasperatingly, the heavens looked the same. I was underwhelmed, denied a more exotic and exciting aspect. As we entered the Gujarat there was a grumble of thunder, gloomy rain-laden clouds scurried into view and a foreboding entered my soul. I glanced at *Rama* and silently prayed. '*Ram, Ram, Ram...*'

We reached the village just after one o'clock on that moonless night. Thunder and forked lightning filled the sky, but it wasn't raining. Our dusty headlights picked out a pair of cows slumbering in the middle of the road. As the brightness hit them they became confused, opened their eyes and blinked, but refused to move. We arced around them and hit an oleander bush, disturbing a yellow snake with oval brown spots. It slithered away from the light into a bed of pink roses.

We parked at the top of a steep road and at once the silence was broken by what sounded like a single gunshot followed by a tumult of shouting and screaming men, the high-pitched wailing of women and babies and the unmistakable thump-thump of *lathis* being used to beat bodies. At rapid intervals the lightning picked out the mayhem at the bottom of the village amid a cluster of mud huts, where a chaotic skirmish was underway. *Lathis* rained blows on bodies cowering on the floor and the cries of pain increased with each strike.

My grandmother, Bhulima, was waiting to greet us. She was a broad formidable woman and her stern face and trademark pristine white clothing made her intimidating: a queen who must be obeyed. She hugged us all, enveloping us in the folds of her flouncing sari, weeping and sniffling with joy. It was the first time she had seen me since I'd left India sixteen years ago.

'It's the *doobras*', she said, nodding her head towards the uproar. 'They've been making illicit alcohol again and someone in the village has tipped off the police and they're making arrests. Why they come at this unearthly hour and why they don't leave those poor people alone, I don't know. What harm are they doing to anyone but themselves? At least we can be certain *Rama* will punish those sadistic officers. But don't worry, it'll be over soon. Come inside.'

She was clearly on the side of the oppressed, but her language shocked me. *Doobra* is a very derogatory local term for *Dalits*, or as they used to be known, untouchables. After independence it became illegal to discriminate against not only the lower castes but also against *Dalits*, who are not even included in the caste system. Clearly the old prejudices were very much alive.

We entered the house. Just inside were two giant green swings suspended on flimsy blue ropes, which served as sofas. They creaked and squeaked as *Ba* and *Bapuji* collapsed on cyan cushions embroidered with fierce blue-green peacocks, sighing with relief as they did so: the twenty-six-hour journey had taken its toll. Tea and *Thums Up*, the *faux* Indian Coca Cola which is fizzier, spicier and nastier than the real thing, were brought in on brass platters by our servants.

We were faced with a gargantuan meal of many colours and aromas. The table was quickly festooned with pea and sultana *kachoris*, crispy aubergine and banana *bhajias, parathas* stuffed with spinach and lilva, okra and potato curries, home-made lime and chilli pickles and three types of *poppadums*, yellow, green and brown. Standing guard on either side were two tall pitchers of fresh juice, almost certainly mango and lime judging by the pile of discarded fruit stones and green and gold peel in the nearby copper bucket. It looked and smelt fantastic, but I wasn't hungry and asked if I could go straight to bed.

'If you are so tired then off you go. I was hoping to show you pictures of some lovely girls I have found for you, but with your flight being delayed it's very late and now is not the best time; so we will discuss your marriage tomorrow, after breakfast.'

*Not if I had anything to do with it.*

Bhulima patted me on the head and ran her fingers though my hair and pointed to my bed in the far corner.

'You can sleep there tonight. It's the quietest place in the house. Oh, and by the way, that modern toilet at the back of house isn't working. Someone's coming to repair it very soon. So use the one outside. There's a torch over there.'

I groaned at the thought of using a hole in the ground. Thankfully I had no need for it tonight.

Before I reached my bed there was another commotion outside. We all dashed out and recoiled as a green and black snake slithered rapidly away, past our front door. It had probably been disturbed by the racket made by the line of men stumbling up the road towards us, some visibly drunk and unsteady on their feet. Overhead an eagle owl screeched at them as it hovered menacingly, furious that its hunting ground had been invaded by an unruly mob and a growing number of onlookers awakened by the din, at a time when all was usually silent. By now the entire village was lit up by the torches of the police, the electric lights of the wealthy and the more dramatic flares and *diwas* of the poor.

The arrested men were tied together with ragged ropes, all bawling and protesting as the police threateningly wielded *lathis* alongside. Occasionally a blow landed, which increased the din. Foul language filled the air and the most common insult, '*benchod*', uttered by both the enforcers and the enforced, echoed around like an aggressive chant in a football stadium. As we watched one prisoner tried to escape but he was quickly and brutally overpowered and shoved back into line, holding his head with both hands as he tried to staunch the flow of blood. Soon they reached the bend leading to the main road to Munsari and as they disappeared round it peace returned to the village.

I shuffled away, exhausted. Gujarati houses are open plan and there is no privacy, no protection from the eyes and noise of others. As I undressed I glanced though the metal bars in the window looking out onto the rear. We had no curtains and the shutters are usually left open to let in the breeze. In the darkness I could see a pair of glowing eyes in the distance looking straight towards me. The body was invisible. Was it a leopard, a lynx, a jackal or perhaps even a tiger? The sighting of a jackal is widely believed to bring bad luck, but I doubted whether an encounter with any of the other creatures in the open would result in better fortune. Despite the constant chatter which reverberated around the house and a cacophony of chirping crickets I was fast asleep within minutes.

I awoke to find the servants were busy cleaning and cooking and my family was nowhere to be seen. In the alcove next to the kitchen area the bright yellow and blue flicker of the ghee-fuelled *diwas* was illuminating our shrine, adding a sense of theatre to the over-elaborately carved dark wooden and stone figures of gods and saints. I had somehow slept through the early morning din, even through the lengthy prayers. I stepped outside and stared at our house in amazement. How was it possible? I distinctly remembered the building as shaped like a square box, painted a pleasant pale yellow and watched over by an army of bright-eyed mongooses, regularly fed with *chappatis* and rice by Bhulima because they kept curious snakes away. But in reality it was a dismal green rectangle with Ionic columns and the volutes at the top were badly damaged, looking as if they might crash down at any moment. Disappointingly, our serpent patrol had vanished and the appearance and rapid disappearance into the rose bush of yet another snake underlined their absence.

There was an air of faded elegance about the old place. The chipped cracked columns and the mosaic of *Krishna* playing his flute next to a cow made it resemble a refugee from the last days of Rome, incongruous in a very Indian village. A scruffy, bearded black-faced monkey clutching a bunch of ripe bananas was hunched on the roof. He stared back at me, screeched a warning as I approached and disappeared from view. In the back garden the corrugated iron toilet was just as I'd pictured it with its sloping roof and rickety creaking door concealing a large hole in the ground surrounded by slimy green bricks and stones. As a child I'd never enjoyed going in there because cheeky brown macaques would suddenly appear and shriek at me deafeningly, as if I were trespassing on their territory. Once one had wrenched a banana I was eating on the verandah out of my hand and enjoyed the fruit of his labour from a treetop, watching me and chattering gleefully.

I peered into the gloom and the stench, as familiar as it was horrendous, hit me like a wave. A squadron of gleaming green and black flies buzzed furiously around my head, persisting even when I waved my arms to fend them off. As I recoiled I almost knocked over the buckled and battered bucket filled with water and the half-empty dull pewter jug perched unevenly on the ground. Inside, two huge red-spotted brown beetles were furiously swimming in unending circles, but I wasn't worried about dealing with them as I had no intention of using water. I held my breath for as long as I could and breathed in intermittently only when I was on the point of fainting. It was a long time since I'd used an Indian toilet, but I knew the rules. Left hand for washing your behind, right hand for eating. But I had changed my habits and had brought a secret supply of toilet paper for emergencies, which I kept in my pockets. Bhulima would be horrified. As soon as I could I escaped and raced away, breathing in lungfuls of jasmine-scented air.

Bhulima strode out, quickening her pace with each step. 'The bathwater is being heated on the fire but it isn't ready yet, it won't be too long,' she said. 'We've used the first batch up already.' Everything she said sounded like an order trumpeted by an angry elephant, but underneath the bluster she was really quite gentle and very kind.

'When did the English toilet stop working?' I asked.

'Two years ago,' she said.

She had always eschewed the mod cons which *Bapuji*, my father, had proudly installed with money he was earning in England. She had never tried the flushing toilet, which had briefly become a tourist attraction. *Bapuji* told me that on the first day more than a hundred people came to see the newest wonder of Ganeshgam. They weren't convinced that it was the future. Bhulima had been withering in her condemnation.

'Answer me this. Can paper clean as well as water?'

'No.'

'So your wonderful British walk around dirty all day, every day. How can that be right? And to think they ruled an Empire with unclean bottoms.'

For weeks after that a trickle of visitors arrived but not one would use the new contraption. Now it was a museum piece, locked away, unseen and unloved. To avoid a diatribe I changed the subject.

'What happened to our pet mongooses?'

'Look overhead,' she said pointing. Huge red kites were circling just below the slate grey clouds, hungrily seeking out any moving creature down below. 'Those bully birds have driven them all away. We don't know why there are so many hawks around at the moment, but everything goes in cycles and the mongooses will return, of that I am sure. They know where the best *chappatis* in the village are, after all.'

'Any news on what happened last night?

'The police fired a gun but it was only to frighten the *doobras* into submission. They were too drunk to fight back because they'd been downing that hooch they make for hours. Why they drink terrible stuff I don't know! They took away eight men and there's a trail of blood to show how brutal they were. I ask you, who will look after their families now?'

As she was speaking it became obvious that Bhulima was in a hurry. She was hopping from foot to foot and abruptly marched off towards the outhouse. As soon as she opened the door the air began to reek of human faeces and I moved hastily away. I spotted my fourth snake sliding up the mango tree and began to wonder how long it would be before I was bitten. '*Ram, Ram, Ram, Ram...*'

I passed under the shade of a pair of neem trees crowded with yellow and red parakeets, perpetually dancing on their toes in excitement. The trees were sacred because they provided protection from the sun and wood for burning and building. They also looked after our dental health. I broke off a twig, but not before making sure there were no lurking serpents lying in wait. The birds screeched angrily but they didn't fly away as they had spotted Bhulima and knew that she always gave them stale *parathas* and nuts. My mouth tasted bitter so I bit on the twig and it released a cloying sweet and sour resin. After a little chewing the twig transformed into a toothbrush, with the resin acting as toothpaste. But it felt like a poor substitute. I threw away my eco-brush and pulled out a stick of chewing gum, feeling vaguely guilty because I'd rejected something so Indian. Had I become a *pukka* westerner? I thought of the England football team's recent failures, their shameful defeats to lowly opposition and how depressed that made me and also of the disastrous Tests against Australia: when we lost I had almost cried with frustration. England and India were due to clash later this summer and I would have loved to go for a beer with the English side. We would have so much in common, so much to discuss; especially with the Leicestershire contingent. The opposition would seem like foreigners, some hardly able to speak English, let alone Gujarati as there are twenty-two recognised languages in India. So why did I want India to win? My divided loyalties left me totally confused.

8

# Chapter 2

## Big rain

Even at this early hour the house was filled with the enticing aroma of roasting fennel and cumin seeds. On the grey stone floor at the back a fire burned fiercely red with little smoke, which was just as well as there was no chimney. Kohli, the youngest of our five servants, was stirring the spices on a hotplate frothing with ghee. She mouthed the traditional greeting, '*Jaisi Krishna.*' I cupped my hands and replied with the same words. She added another spice and my nostrils began to twitch and my throat burned as I caught the unmistakeable reek of *hing,* which my father always called devil's dung. I would often complain about the odour when I was a child but Bhulima insisted that *hing* is brilliant for digestion and it was thrown into almost every meal. We rarely had stomach problems, although we did belch a lot. Bhulima had an answer for that: 'Better out than in.'

A four foot tall triangular mountain of ripening orange mangoes marked the boundary between the kitchen and the rest of the house. As a child I had been dwarfed by the pile. Mangoes have always been my favourite fruit and an image of myself as a three-year-old flashed before my eyes.

My face was covered in a thick messy layer of mango pulp as I tackled my favourite part of the fruit, the *goatlee*: the stone always reserved for the youngest in the family to suck and lick until no flesh is left on it. After all these years I could smell and feel the delight of that moment.

Beside the mangoes, on a sky blue painted table with carved legs which resembled standing snakes, sat a mahogany radio almost half the size of a washing machine. It was richly-grained and had a gleaming gold metal band all the way round the top and bottom and a handsome speaker grill covering two thirds of the face, made from woven cloth. Underneath was a rectangular frequency dial with ivory knobs on either side for tuning and volume control. At the bottom sat four push-buttons marked AM, FM and SW and ON/OFF. It had four short legs and a sticker with lurid red script proclaiming its one year guarantee and country of manufacture, England. It was a work of art worthy of prominent display, quite unlike the black plastic gadget we had at home, a tenth its size and made in China. We were the first in the village to have a radio and it was the second wonder of the house, after the flushing toilet, attracting curious visitors from neighbouring villages. When I was two years old *Bapuji* had gone alone to Africa to work. Two years later he returned for a brief visit, wilting under the weight of the cardboard box containing the mysterious device capable of bringing music and voices here from afar.

I switched it on and it took an age to warm up and for the green light to flicker on. I could picture the moment I heard my first news broadcast, the whole family and invited guests standing agog around the magic contraption. There were floods in Surat and a woman had a baby in a tree while seeking refuge from the waters. I had wondered if they had to catch it like a cricket ball when it popped out.

*Ba* had been visiting neighbours and she returned to find me peering into the back of the radio.

'It was so exciting when we first switched it on. There were so many people here, it was like a crowd at the cricket match. You have a good memory for all sorts of things. Do you remember the first time we heard the news?'

'Only the woman having a baby in the tree.'

'Yes , that's the sort of story that stays with your forever. Who can forget that once you've heard it? You asked so many questions. Where would they get baby clothes if they were stuck up a tree? How would they clean up the poo? Would they have any toys with them?'

'So what else happened that day?'

'I remember it so clearly. They began with fears about India and Pakistan going to war in Kashmir. There were always fears in those days, just like now. Then there was a train crash in Uttar Pradesh where lots died, more than a hundred. And the Indian cricket team lost to England, so *Bapuji* was very depressed. He said he wished he hadn't bought the radio when he heard that and we all laughed because he looked so dejected. And Bhulima grumbled because the radio was bringing so much sadness into our home, but I think that secretly she was proud *Bapuji* could afford to buy the latest technology. We all were.'

Suddenly the green light came on and the radio crackled into life. After all these years the news was as dismal and familiar as ever. There had been a bombing in Kashmir killing forty and injuring hundreds and there were fears that India and Pakistan might square up to one other once more. Flooding in Bangladesh and north India was the worst for fifty years making hundreds of thousands homeless. Inflation was high and the rupee was losing value. The Indian cricket team had lost again, this time to the West Indies. It was lucky *Bapuji* had gone out.

I turned the dial and found nothing but a stream of Bollywood songs and mournful religious laments. I longed to hear Queen or Pink Floyd or sports news from England. Who had triumphed at Wimbledon? Who had won the Grand Prix? Had Leicestershire made it to the Benson and Hedges Cup Final at Lord's? Had Leicester City signed any new players? I had asked a friend to save copies of the Leicester Mercury for me and would have to wait until I got home to find out. Home was no longer the colourful sunny village of Ganeshgam in the Gujarat. Home was five thousand miles away, a dreary, rain-soaked city in the East Midlands where we lived in an ugly terraced house which struggled to keep out the cold and damp and where the windows were so small it was always dark inside and the fluorescent lights were on even at the height of summer. Why was I so keen to get back?

I felt hot and dirty so I headed for the bathhouse. That was our grandiose name for what was a dilapidated old cowshed. Outside, the servants had finally heated up more hot water over an open fire in a huge, decaying and dangerous-looking pan with handles on each side. I used a jug to fill a bucket and went inside. Nothing had changed. The crumbling stone building with the uneven terracotta floor tiles was just as I had left it: dark, damp and dismal. As I entered I could hear echoes of my past. Each morning I would bathe here with *Ba* and in between the splashing she often sang the Indian national anthem, *'Jaya Gana Mana'*. I couldn't recall the words but the chorus came streaming back:

*'Jaya he, jaya he, jaya he Jaya jaya jaya, jaya he!'*

'Victory, victory to thee!'

Would an English mother ever sing 'God Save the Queen' at bathtime? I doubted it. Perhaps the clue lies not in the words but in the tune: one is catchy and joyful, the other a dirge.

There was running cold water and an extra empty bucket. I mixed hot and cold water to a suitable temperature, stood up and poured jugfuls over myself until I was thoroughly wet. Then I scrubbed myself with green carbolic soap, massaged shampoo into my hair and rinsed it all away. The exhilarating moment was emptying the remaining water over my head in one huge *whoosh*. Like the big dipper at a fairground it never failed to thrill.

Inside the house the sofas were swinging wildly. Occupying them were Bhulima and my parents, who had been trying to explain my bizarre choice of university course. Bhulima was baffled.

'I know your parents are very proud of you, but why are you studying German and Russian? Do you not want to become a doctor or an engineer? Those are good professions for a proper Gujarati boy. What is the use of German? Or *Russian*.' It was an excellent question and I had no answer.

Thankfully the conversational thread was broken by Kohli's mother, Amisha, arriving with *masala chai*, made by boiling half-milk, half-water in a pan set over an open fire and adding sugar and a *masala* mix of cloves, cinnamon, cardamom and nutmeg. The milk came warm, fresh and unpasteurised from the cow's udder on our farm. Amisha hugged me for a full minute, refusing to let go even when I tried to pull away.

'Oh, how you've grown! You look just like your father. Do you remember my husband, Chetladada? He passed away last year - you were always his favourite. He made you kites and you destroyed them as quickly as he could make them! He always talked about you and hoped you would visit. It's such a shame it's taken you so long to come home. If only...'

'Chetladada was tiny,' *Bapuji* interrupted, 'but stronger than an ox. In the monsoon season when the streets were flooded he used to collect me from school and carry me through the water on his shoulders to keep me dry. He brought me pistachio *pendas* because I was always hungry.'

'And whenever anyone got seriously ill when the village was flooded we sent him to fetch the doctor, because we couldn't use the rickshaw,' said Bhulima. 'He'd walk four miles through the deep waters there and back and return with the doctor carrying his medicine bag high above his head. Now there is a family right in the middle of the village who have a phone, so we can just call the doctor.'

Amisa's eyes filled with tears at the memories. 'He was a great man and a great husband. We miss him every day, every minute.'

Overcome, she scuttled away to remove all traces of her embarrassment and returned with Kohli, bringing breakfast: dark yellow turmeric and cumin *pooris, chevro* and hot mango pickled in red chillis and fenugreek, Bhulima's speciality. The servants did all the washing and peeling but she always added the spices and final touches.

She quizzed us for the next hour about friends and relatives, our health and our plans for our month in India. Then I noticed her inserting her hands deep into the folds of her sari, either to scratch or, more likely, search for hidden objects. I had a premonition that she was looking for the stash of photos of her 'lovely girls' so that I could choose a wife. A fresh wave of *hing* hit me, making me cough and splutter and in need of fresh air, so I seized my chance to escape. On the verandah I discovered a *charpoy*, a bed of thin ropes strung across a wooden frame. *Charpoy* is Hindi for four legs, but this one had three and a half and was on the point of collapse. In the months of intense heat Bhulima would sleep out here and most days she would sit and gossip with anyone passing.

The heat was turning my head hazy; my mind meandered out of control, like a drunk crossing a road. Bhulima's gossiping had filled my head with a litany of Hindi and Sanskrit words which have passed into English: bungalow, juggernaut, pyjama, cummerbund, gymkhana, bazaar, jodhpur, khaki and best of all, doolally. I lay there wondering whether the mental hospital for mad soldiers in Doolally was still going. How did people live and work in such heat? Bhulima had told me that last week the temperature reached forty-seven degrees. Today it was a mere thirty-five. In England a twelve-degree drop would usually mean switching the heating back on. I roused myself and walked slowly and deliberately down the street, hoping that this would prevent me from reaching boiling point, but the humidity was sky high and I felt damp, sticky and more uncomfortable with every step. My shirt and trousers were clinging to my body like large limpets. I heard a rumble of thunder but it sounded very faint and distant.

'*Kem cho?*'

'*Saru che.* '

'How are you?'

'Fine, thanks.'

The greeting was constant and the reply automatic. Everybody knew me, but I didn't know them. I was the son of Dahyabhai Morarji Patel and the grandson of the loud, much-loved and respected village elder, Bhuliben Morarji Patel. Many Hindu women carry their husband's name and sons and daughters their father's.

'*Mane orkhay?*'

'Do you know me?'

I had no idea who she was but out of politeness replied yes, of course. The gnarled old woman sitting under the banyan tree was leaning on a knobbly walking stick and picking her teeth ferociously with a piece of straw. A tiny but obstinate green object, anything from fennel to chilli to coriander, had lodged between her two yellow sloping teeth and she was struggling to poke it out. She continued hacking away as she spoke, gurning hideously at me.

'*Maru nam su che?*'

'What's my name then?'

I smiled and said I'd forgotten. She seemed genuinely upset that I didn't know her. She was Hemama, Bhulima's best friend, and she used to bounce me up and down on her knees. I shuddered at the idea. She was very thin and sharp-boned and it must have been very uncomfortable.

'You were a very determined baby and always got what you wanted. You pulled the most magnificent *jibroo* when you didn't. Do you remember that?'

A *jibroo* is when you turn your lower lip inside out so it hangs down in an ugly and unpleasant way, rather like sticking your tongue out but using your lip instead. It is a common way of showing dissatisfaction for badly-behaved toddlers in Ganeshgam.

'No. That was a long time ago.'

'Well, you're certainly a big boy now. Bhulima tells me she's found some lovely girls for you, the very best available. I hope you'll be very happy.'

Like Bhulima she assumed I had come to India to find a wife. She was wrong. We had flown over to attend the wedding of my cousin Urmila and I was determined to fight any plans to turn me into a bridegroom. I mumbled something about having to get to a relative's house and walked away. Before long a man in a starched white Nehru suit stopped me and issued a weather warning. He had a long face like a parrot and a wondrous hooked nose which almost covered his mouth. 'Big rain,' he hissed. 'Big rain coming, very big. You must take cover.'

'Which way to the school?' I asked him. 'Is it that way?' I pointed to the right. He looked at me blankly so I repeated my question more loudly and he nodded, his head making a figure of eight as he did so, an annoying Indian trait which means both yes and no. I gesticulated vigorously to the right and began walking in that direction. His head continued to bob up and down and sideways, but he didn't shout after me so I assumed I had guessed correctly. His prophecy was swiftly realised as within minutes the monsoon clouds began unloading their considerable burden. I stepped up onto a nearby verandah and peered into the house though the iron bars on the window. There seemed to be nobody at home and it was very sparsely furnished. Suddenly I spotted a portly figure staring straight back at me from the gloom, the whites of the eyes shining, the rest of the body almost hidden by the darkness. Embarrassed, I was about to avert my gaze when I realised it was a life-size statue of *Ganesh*, guarding the house. As my eyes adjusted to the darkness within I could make out his elephant trunk coming down in a straight line and curling gently to the left.

15

Thunder and lightning filled the air. For a minute the monsoon rains trickled down gently then increased in volume until they crashed with a terrifying roar, like a waterfall cascading directly from the skies. The raindrops were heavy and made a drumming sound on the rooftops and surged down into the streets. Within thirty minutes the area was flooded as the drainage was poor or non-existent.

Bare-footed children in a rainbow of bright-coloured shirts and shorts ran outside and fell into the water, by now six inches deep, splashing themselves and each other and squealing in delight. A drainpipe was loose on the front of the dun-coloured bungalow opposite and a father and son come out fully clothed to stand under the tumbling water, relishing their alfresco power-shower. Their shouts of joy filled the street, but I was the only one who noticed them. I was stuck there for an hour and a half, never bored as I watched a variety of water games played out in front of me. A pair of boisterous bullocks joined in the revelry, lowering their heads in sheer ecstasy into what had now become a fast-flowing stream. The water was slowly turning a murky reddish brown as it collected the clay and dust and remnants of dried mud and dung from the pot-holed ground. Then as suddenly as it came the rain stopped, which was fortunate for the *Dalits* living at the bottom of the village as severe flooding often washed away their mud huts. The rich at the top of the hill were protected by the laws of gravity. I rolled up my trousers and ventured into the warm water. Would I catch some foul disease? The children and the bullocks seemed happy enough so I decided to risk it. *'Ram, Ram, Ram...'*

Could I find my way to my old school? Surely it was left at the bottom of the road and first right. It turned out to be right and second left. The gate was locked so I jumped over it. Half-gnawed ripe gold and red guavas and baby green mangoes littered the yard. Which creatures had been nibbling them? Chipmunks? I could see a group gawking at me on the far wall. Monkeys? Wild boars? A high pitched hooting accompanied by constant chatter and a distant grunting told me they were not far away. I made my way to my old classroom and looked through the window into a bare room with a blackboard, a cupboard for the books and slates and chalk in the far corner. No desks and no chairs. We always sat on the floor and nothing had changed. I shut my eyes and was five again. On my first day we had all gathered outside and the teacher, Ashwinbhai, was very agitated. The veins on his head were throbbing with excitement as if worms were slithering around inside, trying to escape. He told us not to move. He went inside and we heard the sound of a *lathi* being whacked repeatedly on the floor with unwavering violence.

He emerged triumphantly, flourishing the *lathi* with a large dead and blood-spattered snake covered in gold diamond shapes. He hurled it into the bushes and we watched as it spun several times in the air before it fell and vanished in the dense foliage. We went in for registration: most of the twenty pupils in the class were Patels, so our first names were called out instead: Anilbhai, Andandkumar, Bharatkumar and so on. Then we were marched outside where we sat in neat rows, said our prayers and loudly and proudly sang *Jaya Gana Mana.* It was time for our first lesson.

'You all saw me kill a snake but there is one you must never kill, and that is the cobra. When Lord Buddha was sleeping a cobra put his head over him to protect him from the sun. To thank him Lord Buddha drew some marks like spectacles over his hood. A cobra in the house is a good omen and it kills vermin, like rats and mice.'

'What is a bad omen?' I asked.

'We Hindus have many. Some say a black cat or an owl on your house will bring bad luck. Others worry that continual hiccups or sneezing three times will mean a very bad illness. I went to the north, to the Himalayas, and they told me the sight of a snake is sure to bring good fortune; but in the south they say it's a very, very bad sign. Who is right? No one knows, so I urge you to take no notice of these things. You must always pray to *Rama* and he will make sure you are safe.'

On that first morning Ashwinbhai told us another story. It was about a massive stone which mysteriously appeared one day and blocked the road between two villages. Carts had to divert through bushes and pedestrians hurt themselves stumbling into it at night, but no one would move it. Then a poor man came across the stone. He was on his way to market to sell his worldly goods so he could buy food for his family and asked people nearby to help him move the stone, but they all refused. He returned to his own village to borrow a horse and cart and ropes and heaved the stone into a ditch. Lying underneath were a thousand rupees. I still feel obliged to remove obstacles wherever I see them, though I have yet to find a penny. It strikes me that the tale may be responsible for causing obsessive-compulsive disorder.

I walked round the school perimeter and in my head could hear ghostly chants of the times tables. We were taught to recite them not just to twelve but to forty. I glanced up at the twin tamarind trees, so close they formed an umbrella against the harsh sun, and counted *shavees* (twenty-six) fruits on a typical branch. There were...*shatrees* (thirty-six) branches, so that meant there were *nav so ne shatrees* (936) tamarinds. The answer came automatically, a Pavlovian reaction. I suddenly realised that I could only do this in Gujarati *because I had never learned them in English*. I translated the answer into what had become my first language.

With my head full of numbers I hurdled over the low gate and made for the village centre, passing three *Dalit* women in lurid green *saris* vigorously thrashing their washing over a rock in the stream. Blue, yellow and red dye was streaking off the clothes and polluting the water. Nearby was a cluster of mud huts, each one with a goat or a cow tethered outside. By one of them lay a woman on a charpoy, who looked as ancient as anyone I had ever seen. Her face was gaunt and almost every bone in her body was prominent; much of her scalp was visible through the few strands of wispy white hair. She was writhing around and moaning softly, but nobody took any notice. A few feet away a woman was grinding a pile of dried vermillion chillis into powder.

'Is she alright?' I asked, pointing at the old woman.

'*Saru, che, saru che,*' she replied, not looking up. 'We are waiting for her to die. We've been waiting for two months. She is ninety-seven.'

Outside the next hut a girl in a bright pink and yellow sari was making *parathas* stuffed with vegetables over a billowing fire. She looked fifteen, but her face was careworn and her eyes exuded sadness. She managed a smile.

'*Kem cho?*'

'*Saru che.*'

I asked her how many people lived in the hut.

'Twelve. My parents, grandparents, my husband, my son and daughter and four brothers.'

I peered inside: it was little more than fourteen feet in diameter. A large puddle had formed near the door after the rain. Another downpour and the hut would quickly be flooded. I tried to imagine how twelve bodies could possibly crowd into such a confined space, let alone sleep in it, but found it impossible. I searched my pockets and found forty rupees, little more than fifty pence, and offered it out of guilt. There was no refusal or false modesty – she grabbed the money and secreted it in her sari.

'Were you here when the police came last night?'

'Yes. They woke us up and searched the hut, smashed up everything.' She lifted a finger towards a pile of broken crockery, shattered bars of wood and flattened metal jugs. 'All those things were thrown about and destroyed by the police. They went into every hut and destroyed everything.

'A few men were drinking outside. They could see we weren't involved because we were asleep, but they woke us up, searched the hut and started chucking things around. What's worse is that or two of the men they took away were just smoking a *bidi* and chatting and they never touch a drop of alcohol; but they still arrested them. So now it's against the law to smoke. They're all *gundas*.'

Tears came to her eyes and I was mortified that I had made her relive the night she was trying to forget. After mumbling some words of solidarity, I shuffled away.

# Chapter 3

## The sadhu

Our village, Ganeshgam, is named after the god *Ganesh*. He was created by the goddess *Parvati* to guard her as she bathed. When her husband *Shiva* returned from battle and was denied access to his bathing wife he cut off the boy's head. Parvati was so upset that *Shiva* sent his warriors to fetch the head of the first dead animal they found, which happened to be an elephant. The head was attached to the boy and he returned to life. His head has come to symbolise knowledge and wisdom and because of his role as Parvati's guardian he is often placed facing doorways to keep out intruders.

*Ganesh*, with his pot belly and flapping ears, is one of the most popular gods in the Hindu pantheon, but I've always been keener on the monkey god *Hanuman*, who helped rescue *Rama* and *Sita* from the demon *Ravana*. He could fly and move mountains and he carried a seriously powerful weapon, a giant mace.

As I turned the corner I saw the only impressive building in Ganeshgam, the *Ganesh Mandir*. I entered through the intricately-carved north door and was overwhelmed by the sandalwood rising from the smoking a*garbattis*. Every minute or so an echoing bell shattered the silence as worshippers announced their arrival to the gods. I rang it and the din deafened me as it resonated around the entrance. It was so loud you could feel the sound.

We all bowed our heads as we approached centre stage. *Diwas* powered by ghee hissed and crackled like fireworks, lighting up the giant marble statue of *Ganesh* wearing magenta trousers and perched on a bright yellow sunflower. On one side were wooden statues of *Rama* and *Sita* in garlands of fresh marigolds, the devoted *Hanuman* kneeling before them; on the other an exquisite turquoise-skinned *Krishna* stood playing his flute: it was difficult not be entranced by his almond eyes and lotus pink lips. A god like this was so much more appealing than the stern white-bearded old man of the Old Testament. And we had so many to choose from! I felt pity for those religions stuck with only one.

It was the smallest figure on the podium, *Hanuman,* who fascinated me most. I recalled the stories I had heard about him: how he had tried to grab the sun because he thought it was a fruit; how he'd travelled from Sri Lanka to India in one giant leap and how he had carried an entire mountain full of medicinal herbs to restore the wounded in *Rama's* army. Every Indian boy I knew wanted to be *Hanuman*. His most astonishing superpower was his ability to expand and contract so that he could become as large as Mount Everest or as small as a fly. We used to watch Bollywood films in which he was outnumbered by an army of apparently invincible demons and he just grew and grew until they ran off in sheer terror. These scenes were always followed by spontaneous applause and I could hear it now in my head and see the delight on everyone's face as good once again triumphed over evil. I felt the disapproving eyes of *Ganesh* searing through my back and looked away. The atmosphere was cloying and humid and claustrophobic, so I went outside and breathed in lungfuls of incense-free air.

The streets were filled with the hubbub of hawkers and beggars and fast food wallahs offering *masala dhosas, samosas, kachoris, bhajias, vadas* and *idlis* for a 'special price'. A girl without legs and arms sat with a begging bowl outside the post office. She was about ten and sat silently, but her large brown eyes pleaded for money. I searched my pockets for spare cash and she acknowledged the gesture with a bow of her head. *Bapuji* told me that some of the child beggars were deliberately maimed by their parents or by gangs who kidnapped orphan children to make them more appealing and bring in extra cash. I hoped this girl was not a victim.

The door to the post office was wide open and inside the fans were whirring and wobbling dangerously in a vain attempt to keep the workers cool. There were six of them squatting on the uneven floor, sorting out bags of mail and parcels, their white shirts damp with sweat. Whenever I wrote to Bhulima the address was simply 'At Post Ganeshgam, District Valsad, Near Surat, India.' That meant the postman had to know every single resident, not just here but in smaller surrounding villages too. Only my uncle had a telephone, so urgent communications arrived via telegram. I moved aside as the telegram *wallah* dashed out, waving a handful of messages conveying births, deaths and all the news from across the globe.

Fifty yards further along was an oval lake where *dhobi wallahs* were thrashing laundry on stones. A solemn group of kingfishers sat watching them from a flat rock jutting out above water level. The flash of shocking turquoise on their wings was the only clue to their identity as they were nothing like their European counterparts. They had beaks twice the size and much of the body was a disappointing orangey brown.

A *dhobi wallah* with a stoop and a limp walked along the shoreline until he reached his allotted stone, weighed down by his huge wicker basket. He stepped into the shallow water, held the basket before him as if he were offering it to the gods, and bowed his head. He mouthed some prayers and then emptied his load of vibrantly-coloured shirts and *saris* into the lake before tossing the basket nonchalantly back over his head onto dry land. Even then the kingfishers didn't fly away.

The *dhobi wallah* applied a mixture of detergent and bleach and then began rhythmically pounding the clothes with surprising violence on the stone. The water changed to murky indigo and I wondered how the fragile buttons on the shirts could survive such a beating. The answer came as one flew into the air and landed back in the water in two pieces. The button *wallah* would be doing good business later. The *dhobi wallah* sensed he was being watched so he turned and stared, straining his eyes. I guessed he was short-sighted but couldn't afford glasses. Suddenly his face lit up and he called out my name.

'Bharatkumar, *kem cho*? Bhuliben told me you were coming to find a wife!'

I was taken aback that news of my arrival had spread. It was clear that in Ganeshgam there were no secrets.

'You won't know me, but I remember you as a child. I am Chandra. We have been *dhobis* to your family even before your grandfather, Morardada, was born, a long, long, long time. Morardada was a great man, brave as a tiger.' He lifted his *dhoti* and showed me an old scar on his leg, at least six inches long. 'Once I was attacked by a jackal and Morardada came to the rescue. It almost bit though my leg and I would have lost it if he hadn't turned up with a *lathi* and beaten it away.'

He spoke about my grandfather with great admiration for several minutes. He was apparently brilliant at sorting out disputes between warring *dhobi wallahs* and his judgements were always respected. He seemed to have been judge and jury on most legal matters in the village. Chandra became so fulsome in his praise that I began to feel embarrassed and changed the subject.

'How do you distinguish between the laundry of one household and another? You must do so many.'

He grinned, revealing a startling array of missing and decaying brown and yellow teeth. 'Each one has a mark in indelible ink. We put it somewhere you can't see it, inside the garment. See, this with the double cross is for your neighbour, Dinubhai Niak and his family. Yours is a circle. The *Brahmins* opposite you have a circle with a dot inside it. I know each and every one off by heart. I'll be round to collect your clothes tonight so we'll have to mark any new ones. Anyway, I must get on. We have extra loads at the moment because of the people arriving for the big wedding '

I watched him working. His movements were strangely soothing and made me feel more relaxed. What would his surname be? Dhobiwallah? I knew the British had given many of those without caste names new surnames for identification purposes, so there were Ginandtonicwallahs and Tiffinwallahs and Sodawallahs, names based on the tasks they performed. The surnames had stuck with the unfortunately-named *wallahs,* who were often unaware of their meaning. I was determined not to change my own name to Husbandwallah. I came out of my reverie as I spotted, beyond Chandra, on the other side of the lake, two boys flying green and yellow kites. Chetladada and I had spent days making and perfecting them until they were ready to reach for the skies. The kites swayed gently in a clockwise motion against a clear blue sky. Suddenly there was a gust of wind. The swirling orange tails clashed and they locked together like dervishes caught in deadly combat and the kites whirled and spun out of control and then came crashing down. The boys laughed and ran off to repair the damage.

Seconds later a gaggle of older boys arrived and started playing *gili danda,* a form of cricket. The *danda* is the longer stick and the *gili* has tapered conical ends. They used the *danda* to draw a circle fifteen yards in diameter in the dust. This was their impromptu pitch. In the centre one of the boys struck the *gilli* on its edge with his *danda* and as it flew into the air he hit it again as hard as he could. The others ran to catch it, but it soared over their heads and the striker was able to make runs by reaching the edge of the circle and back before the danda was retrieved. Fifteen years ago I was one of those boys.

My delight at the game was abruptly broken as a *sadhu* came hurrying towards me, smashing his crooked staff onto the ground at every other step. I was a boy again, overcome with fear and breaking into a cold sweat. His face was painted with white horizontal stripes and he had a red vertical stripe down the centre of his face. He had sleek black oiled hair, neatly held in a bun on top of his head by a saffron ribbon which fluttered menacingly in the breeze and he wore flowing saffron robes to match. Rearing up from behind his neck, rising from his shoulder and peering around his right ear, was a metal cobra with painted red eyes and a forked tongue. I instinctively ducked behind a pair of bullocks tethered outside a mud hut. I'd had a terror of *sadhus* since Bhulima told me they took away children who did not behave. This one looked particularly fierce, with his straggly beard and hooked nose. I was twenty-one and scared of a man smaller than me.

I watched as he went from door to door with his brass begging pot, pleading for food and in return for his blessings and prayers. There are five million of them in India, each on a pilgrimage to achieve enlightenment by leading an ascetic life, wandering from *ashram* to *ashram*. In the larger cities they are usually told to go away, but in rural India there is genuine fear that this will lead to bad luck and possibly even to death. The *sadhu* never goes hungry.

Back at our house Bhulima told me off for disappearing. 'I so wanted us to discuss your marriage, but now your *Ba* and *Bapuji* have gone to see Harishkaka in Munsari and won't be back till late. They wanted you to go with them, but you'd gone! Harish will be so disappointed, but the rickshaw was waiting and they couldn't find you anywhere. Please don't disappear again without telling us where you are going.' She was becoming angry, so to distract her I told her about Chandra and also about the *sadhu.*

'All children need discipline; otherwise they get out of control. The *sadhu* was the best weapon we had to make you behave when it became impossible to reason with you. It was the same with your sister. Kumud used to eat mud, we never found out why. She loved it as much as she loved *kulfi. S*he was a strange girl. We would find her knee-deep in mud with it spread all over her face and the biggest smile you've ever seen. We couldn't stop her! But the threat of the *sadhu* was enough. One mention and she'd leave the mud. Until the next day.'

No matter how Bhulima spoke it seemed to me that she was bellowing. It was one of her less endearing traits.

'Do you remember when we went to see Amratkaka in Dhoopal? You'd been a nuisance throughout the journey and we were losing our tempers in the heat. We could not stop you crying. You wanted *kulfi* and you wanted it straight away, even though there was none available. We came across a *sadhu* with his body buried neck-deep in the earth, chanting verses from the *Bhagwad Gita*. We told you that if didn't behave he would bury you alongside and keep you there until you promised to be a good boy. Your conduct changed instantly. You were so polite all day.

'Oh, you did have a lot of tantrums! It was our fault - we spoilt you rotten because you were the first child and you acted like a little prince. We hadn't seen a *sadhu* for many days so we devised a clever little plan.' Besides its volume, her voice had a concrete mixer quality, shattering the peace whenever she opened her mouth. She cast about for another of my sins.

'You refused to wear clothes which had been laundered - you insisted everything had to be new. So Chandra washed and ironed them and we asked him to put them in a nice bag and give them to Chetladada, so he could pretend he'd been shopping. But you were clever, you noticed a broken button on your shirt and when you realised you'd been deceived you cried and cried. Eventually we put you on top of that cupboard and it was two hours before you stopped wailing. *Ba* was terrified you'll fall and break your neck, but I stood firm and we cured you of your mania.'

The reminiscences came to end as she suddenly let out a prolonged groan and arched her back. She began rubbing the base of it with both hands.

'What's the matter, what have you done?'

'Do you remember how you used to walk on my back when it hurt? I'd like you to do it now.'

'But I was only a toddler.'

'I can take it. I desperately need it, so on you go. Hurry!'

She sprawled on the bed on her enormous belly. The bed grumbled and creaked under the burden and I jumped up and gingerly and reluctantly stepped onto her back. It was a circus balancing act and I had to grab hold of the wall with both hands to stop myself falling. She moaned in ecstasy or agony. It was difficult to tell which. As Bhulima's soft flesh wobbled under my feet I had the feeling of being caught in a quagmire. It would be difficult to reach terra firma: ahead lay the delicate matter the arranged marriage I needed to avoid. Bhulima was a difficult and determined woman, desperate to find me a suitable girl.

# Chapter 4

## The poppadum party

**N**ext morning I was awoken by raucous and tuneless singing, a signature of our entire family. Bhulima and my parents were doing their *puja.* They had already had their baths and lit the *diwas* and now flowers and fruits were being offered to the gods in the household shrine. Accompanying the discordant *bhajans* and prayers was the ringing of hand bells. Bhulima's voice and clanging were more forceful than anyone else's. Wherever they were, the gods were sure to hear her and were unlikely to be pleased, let alone placated.

I cursed the designers of rural Gujarati houses who produce one giant room divided only by obstacles like the mango pyramid, swinging sofas and randomly-positioned single beds. Blue and green cupboards and cabinets decorated with faint yellow flowers were positioned along the walls. Overhead a line of strategically-placed ceiling fans, whirring and creaking day and night, ensured the heat didn't become unbearable. There was no privacy, no hiding-place. There were gods everywhere, in every form: as idols, on hanging carpets or in pictures, all with a common trait, the red *tilak* dotted on their foreheads as a mark of respect. Every one of them seemed to be watching me.

It was six o'clock and still dark outside. The servants had lit a fire but it wasn't bright enough to light the way to the Hindu Hellhole. Using a torch I hastened to the squat stinking toilet, armed with my secret paper roll, held my breath and began to count. My lungs bursting, I reached a hundred and one before I was forced to allow the foul stench to invade my body. This was no place to linger over a book or magazine, which was regrettable as trips here are seldom quick in India due to the extreme high-fibre diet.

As a rosy dawn broke I had already bathed and eaten a cold breakfast. It was *tari hiri* and for twenty hours everything we ate had to be pre-prepared and eaten cold. *Ba* had taken a *bathha* when she became convinced my sister Kumud, then three, had contracted smallpox and became hysterical. It was chickenpox, but *Ba*'s medical knowledge was slight. She prayed to *Rama* and made a pact that if he cured her daughter she would eat no hot food on *tari hiri* day for the rest of her life. Every woman in Ganeshgam had taken a similar *bathha* and we were all condemned to eat cold food one day a year. A lot of miracles had happened here. The pre-cooked *kachoris* and crispy *bhajias* had lost none of their flavour, but I was desperate for hot tea and had to make do with *Thums Up* for my early caffeine dose. Replete and trying not to belch like Bhulima I sat on the *charpoy* and watched the village coming to life.

A pair of wild boars was scavenging in a pile of rubbish, their snouts bobbing up and down in delight when they identified anything edible. Cows and bullocks wandered by themselves along the street and lay down in the middle of the road when they felt tired. One of them belched loudly in unison with me. That would be my last ever *Thums Up*. I took a *bathha* there and then that if I ever drank the repulsive concoction I would give a hundred pounds to charity.

Happily the arranged marriage was off the menu for now as *Ba* and *Bapuji* were going shopping and Bhulima was busy preparing for a *poppadum* party she had arranged. My cousin Urmila, whom we called Ummi, was getting married in two days and she had been invited, along with Bhulima's close female friends and relatives. Out of curiosity I decided to accompany them rather than go with my parents. Bhulima was surprised but said it would be fine as long as I kept out of the way. I'd heard of the famous Ganeshgam *poppadum* parties but had never seen one and it would be a chance to catch up with Ummi.

We still had two hours free so I decided to pay Amisa and Kohli a visit.

They had finished their early chores and gone for a short rest. They lived in an identical adjoining house, which also belonged to us. The difference was startling. There were no beds, just blankets neatly folded on the floor to mark each sleeping place, and no furniture apart from a couple of old cupboards and rickety chairs we had thrown out. Everything they had was dotted sparsely around the edges and the centre was a vast empty space, with a kitchen area and utensils at the back. There was no electricity so there were no fans and they lit oil lamps at night. We paid their meagre wages, just a few rupees a day, and provided them with food, clothes and medicines. With no qualifications and no welfare state they were as tied to us as medieval peasants were to their lords and masters, poor and landless. They belonged to the class Bhulima dismissed as *doobras,* though she was extremely fond of those belonging to our family. Caste divides people according to profession and education and determines whom you can marry, retaining the status quo for the benefit of those higher up the ladder.

At the bottom of the pile and outside the caste system, sat the untouchables or *Dalits*, Sanskrit for downtrodden. They did the dirtiest jobs and drew the shortest straws. There are more than two hundred million of them in India, three times the population of the United Kingdom, and most suffer daily discrimination. Many high caste Hindus refuse to touch anything Dalits have handled and some *Brahmins* will not walk in their shade because they consider it unclean.

I felt a kinship with Amisa now I had returned here from England, for in the 1960s and 1970s, the early days of south Asian migration, *Bapuji* and our relatives could find only menial jobs. In Africa my father had been an accountant, but in England, despite his high level of education, he could only get a job in a knitwear factory. When I started school I was an object of great interest, but some children wouldn't come near me. On a daily diet of garlic and *hing* I reeked of unpleasant and mysterious odours which made me an unwelcome close companion and even now, very occasionally, that sense of rejection lingered. It had given me a taste of what it is to be an outcast.

Remarkably, Amisa and Kohli appeared to feel no envy. They accepted their lot as the will of God, which I found deeply sad. They both greeted me warmly and excitedly asked about England. They had never travelled more than a few miles so even Mumbai was a foreign land.

'What is snow like?' asked Kohli. 'Is it like little *kulfis* falling out of the sky?' An image of plummeting pistachio ice cream cones floated through my head.

Amisa had two sons and a daughter who all worked on our farm and they had left at dawn to plough the fields and milk the cows. As we chatted her elder son, 17-year-old Jitenda, returned with an *undhiyu,* a mixed vegetable dish which filled my nostrils with the heady aroma of coconut and fenugreek. It translates as 'upside down' because that is how it is cooked, buried in an earthenware pot and heated by a fire above. Chetladada once took me to the fields to show me how he made it, but I had long since forgotten the recipe.

'I've also cooked lots for Bhulima,' he said. 'We lit the fire last night, just before sunset, and it's ready to eat now. The longer you leave it the better it tastes because all the flavours meld beautifully. It is truly the best of all dishes. '

Jitenda seemed grown up for a seventeen-year-old, certainly more mature than I was at that age. Working on the farm must be a steep learning curve. I could barely wire a plug or change a fuse, but he could milk cows, plough the fields with oxen and cook *undhiyu*. He couldn't decline German or Russian verbs, but he was definitely more use to society.

Chetladada's family had been our servants for as long as anyone could remember. They were devoted to our family and unlike Dickens' Oliver never asked for more. I wondered what would happen to them if we were not here. Would they be happier because they were free or sad because they no longer had work and a home?

'I have to go back,' Jitenda said. 'The bullock cart needs repairing and it has to be ready for tomorrow.'

As he turned to go a young boy wearing only torn trousers and a pink sweatband almost crashed into him.

'Amishama, something terrible has happened. Horidada has been arrested and he's in jail.'

'Why?'

'We don't know. Those *gunda* policemen took him away last night. He's never touched alcohol but they're saying he's been making *desi daru*. They took away everyone who was awake and he was only smoking a *bidi.' Desi daru* is a bootleg liquor which can contain toxic levels of methanol.

'We must tell Bhuliben straight away,' said Amisha. 'She will know what to do.' She turned to me. 'Horidada is my uncle. He helps us out on the farm and Bhuliben has known him all her life. They were born in the same week.'

Twenty minutes later Bhulima and I boarded a passing rickshaw and headed for the police station. It resembled a temporary barracks which has been under enemy fire and is about to fall down. The façade was full of holes of varying sizes, some large enough to peer through into the gloomy interior. Every window had metal bars and grey-green mould was growing over every dirty wall. Giant insects intent on taking over the building were on the march through every gap and crevice.

Inside a fan was slowly whirring and creaking, powered by just enough electricity to keep it moving. It was positioned directly above a desk piled with files, behind which a police officer was furiously swatting flies and wiping great globules of sweat off his forehead with a filthy handkerchief. He looked like a man spoiling for a fight, not just with the insects plaguing him but with anyone who happened to walk in. He was tall and muscular with a Hitler-style moustache and a patch over his left eye. The sight of Bhulima, the village elder, provoked a transformation and he forced a smile.

'Bhuliben, *jaisi Krishna*. How can I be of service?'

'For a start you can release Hori, right now.'

'But he faces charges of making *desi daru* and you know how strict the government is. We have orders from the regional governor to clamp down on illicit alcohol and we can't afford to go easy on those who break the law. '

There followed a shouting session, with Bhulima doing all the shouting and the police officer and then his superior, who had arrived to see what was going on, listening and cowering. Bhulima's influence was greater than I knew: the police clearly feared her more than the regional governor and soon Horidada was released without charge.

He was a thin man with a thinner moustache. He wore a string vest and a *dhoti* and he reminded me of pictures of prisoners of war I had seen in history books, released after years of confinement. His ribs protruded but despite his frail appearance he had a jutting chin and determined face which showed he was no pushover. He wept with joy as he hugged Bhulima and repeatedly thanked her. What could he ever do to repay her? She said that one day soon he could make one of his famous *undhiyus*, the best in the Gujarat, and they would eat it together with a *masala chai*. He beamed at her and said he would be delighted. She turned to me.

'You wait till you try it. I can't work out what his secret ingredient is and he won't tell anyone. I can't explain it, but it gives you a really happy feeling, unlike anything else! There is no other food in the world which makes you laugh, such is the joy it brings.' I thought of suggesting that she could be ingesting illegal substances, but decided not to spoil her pleasure. Horidada might be teetotal, but evidence suggested he wasn't averse to stronger substances in his *bidis* and *undhiyus*. We dropped Hariadada off outside his house and returned, just in time for the *poppadum* party.

It was a minute's walk to the largest house in the village at the top of our road, its location symbolic of the caste system. High up were the best houses occupied by the haves, the *Brahmins,* Desais and Patels, and lowest down were the mud huts. When the monsoon was severe the homes of the poor were washed away and had to be rebuilt. The water didn't linger at the top.

Cousin Ummi was delighted to see me: 'So good to see a western face.'

'What do you mean, western? I'm still a *pukka* Gujarati boy.'

'You know what I mean. They're all so Indian here, so proper, and I would kill for a beer or a glass of really cold Chardonnay. Not a drop of alcohol! Haven't had any for ten days.'

'Do they know you drink like a fish?'

'I don't. Well maybe like a minnow.'

'Does anyone here know that not only do you drink but you eat more meat than a tiger?'

'Of course not. They'd be horrified.'

34

For inexplicable reasons, with very few exceptions, Gujarati men in England had become carnivores, though for religious reasons they never ate beef, and they also drank alcohol; but the women were mostly strict vegetarians and teetotal. Ummi was an exception, which is why all the boys liked her.

'Trust us to be born in just about the only state where alcohol and meat are banned and all because Mahatma Gandhi was born up the road. Because he was vegetarian and teetotal we all have to follow him. Imagine if he'd been a Punjabi: they'd all be drinking water and *lassi* and *faluda* and eating *dhal* and rice while we in the Gujarat would be eating *tandoori* chicken and downing whisky and beer. We really have a raw deal.'

'That may explain why the Punjabis look much happier and our lot are so serious and miserable.'

We laughed and I was about to tell her about Hori and the *desi daru* arrests when we were accosted by a dozen gnarled old women, all of them bent forward and all asking relentless questions: *Do you remember me? What is my name? You played with my son and my granddaughter. Look there she is now, all grown up. Surely you haven't forgotten her?* Happily Bhulima came to the rescue by announcing that the *poppadum* party was about to begin.

There were no drinks, no balloons, no cakes, not even any edible *poppadum*s. Every six months or so Bhulima would round up her best friends and their daughters to make an array of *poppadum*s from scratch: yellow ones made with a variety of flours and flavours like ginger and cumin or red chilli and garlic or black pepper and green chilli; green ones called *thamta* made with moong flour, which reeked of *hing* and coriander, and the brown rice flour ones, *khitchya*, which packed the biggest spice and chilli punch and were twice as thick as normal *poppadum*s. *Khitchya* had the advantage of being a meal in themselves, uncooked, so there was no need to provide party food. Everyone just helped themselves to the *khitchya* mix, adding peanut oil to moisten the thick dough. It was perfect for *tari hiri* as it had been made the day before and can be eaten cold.

As the party progressed in the dusty yard behind the house I noticed that the bent elders had become spectators. They were the *motimas*, great and great-great-grandmothers, all with alarming gaps in their teeth. They perched under the neem tree, leaning on their crooked sticks, chewing betel leaves filled with sweet syrup and fennel and sipping *masala* tea. I recalled the story of an old woman in Leicester who had died and not been found for two weeks. That couldn't happen here. Everyone lived in large family groups, deprived of privacy and ever unable to avoid company.

There was an easy-going friendship between the women, borne of familiarity from birth. The gossip and laugher was constant and loud, but not forceful enough to put off a jackal, which appeared seeking its lunch. Hindus rarely turn away animals so a servant was dispatched to the house to fetch *chappatis*. I had the feeling it would prefer chunks of meat, but it would have had to travel hundreds of miles to a neighbouring state to find someone serving up chicken or lamb. It stood patiently until it was thrown torn pieces of *chapattis* and chunks of *paneer*, which it devoured before they hit the ground. The jackal licked its chops and slunk silently away into the woods beyond.

Moments later a parakeet landed on Bhulima's shoulder. She didn't seem perturbed as it pecked gently at her ears. She beckoned the servant again and more pieces of *chappati* appeared until the parakeet fluttered away, replete.

The party women sat in a large circle, their *saris* billowing occasionally in the breeze. The elders wore white, the younger ones fashionable multi-coloured ones, some with tiny mirrors sown into the fabric, others with geometric patterns or embroidered suns and moons. Each had a circular wooden board and a rolling pin, thick in the middle and tapered at both ends. In a few seconds they rolled out perfectly-shaped *poppadums*, their actions rhythmic, their chatter unremitting and interrupted only by bouts of giggles. Servants took the floppy *poppadums* and laid them flat to dry. Old *saris*, every colour imaginable, were stretched out wherever there was space: in the garden, on the verandah and alongside entrances. From a low-flying aircraft passengers would think that perfectly circular holes had been dug over a vast area. These holes would keep everyone in *poppadums* for the next six months; until the next party.

# Chapter 5

## The Wedding

It was the day before the wedding and even though I wasn't the groom I was filled with dread at the idea of marrying a stranger. Bhulima was sure to bring up the subject of my marriage now one was taking place right on our doorstep and she was puffed up with the joy of finding a partner for her darling grandson. Her dour demeanour gave way to beaming smiles, indicating confidence that one of her 'lovely girls' would enter her family and deliver great-grandchildren for her delectation.

The first item on the crowded wedding agenda was the *mendhi* ceremony, when Ummi's hands and feet were painted with a mixture of henna, water, lemon juice and eucalyptus oil. As the reddish-brown concoction was applied via a small plastic cone with a tiny hole at the bottom, a group of old *kakis* sang a medley of familiar, strangely hypnotic hymns and prayers accompanied by a *tabla* drummer and a sitarist. Another *kaki*, a talented artist, worked tirelessly until Ummi was covered in exquisite brown and black peacocks and lotus flowers. For the first half hour I was fascinated, but *ennui* set in when I realised I had been watching for hours.

I pondered how many aunts and uncles it is possible to have. In the Gujarat there is a never-ending stream as anyone older, even if unrelated, becomes your *kaki or kaka.* The eldest become grandads or grandmas, *dadas* or *mas.* In the crowded house I counted sixty-three of these four species. I was running out of ways to entertain myself. My Gujarati was good but limited to everyday issues and it would be difficult to strike up conversations about politics or even cricket, as I had no idea what a silly point or bouncer was in my native language. I could understand a lot more than I could express. As a language student I found it odd that I could discuss the philosophies of Nietzsche, Schopenhauer and Leibnitz in German, but not in Gujarati. There was no escape, no wandering off to explore without causing an incident and arousing the wrath of Bhulima. Everyone in the village wanted to ask me the same questions and I spent the morning repeating the same replies. Yes, England was cold and wet. Yes, the education was good and, best of all, free. Yes, we ate imported *pukka* Gujarati food and not boiled and tasteless vegetables like the English did and yes, I was hoping Bhulima would find me a good wife very soon. *What else could I say?*

A number of other wedding rituals were taking place but I had ceased paying attention. I have a memory of a *puja* session dedicated to *Ganesh,* to ensure that the couple would enjoy trouble-free lives and enjoy great fortune. A stronger impression is the sheer length of it, the monotony. I had a claustrophobic sense of being somewhere I no longer belonged. The heat was oppressive and, for the first time in my life, I longed for the cool of an English spring day. I felt I had landed in a foreign land. Was it my fault? Or the fault of my parents for taking me west to embrace English customs and traditions?

The next morning I walked out onto the verandah as a red sun peeped over the horizon. The hubbub of the previous day had died down and there was an air of calm which felt soothing. As I stepped out, a dark grey silhouette was blocking the light. Mimi, the village elephant, was lumbering down the street with a *howdah* wobbling precariously on her back. Bhulima always maintained that if you don't instantly smile whenever you see an elephant there is something wrong with you and she was right, because everyone was grinning. Mimi's forehead bore a shiny red *tilak,* fully three inches in diameter and surrounded by *swastikas,* though these ancient symbols of peace were yellow and not sinister Nazi black. She wore an ornate drape made by a seventy-year-old man known to us all as Hathikaka, which loosely translates as Uncle Elephant. His mother and father had been the first tailors in Ganeshgam and they had passed their skills on to him.

Behind Mimi was a traffic jam as a bullock cart and a pair of camels were held up by the slow-moving elephant.

*Bapuji* told me Hathikaka had customers all over the Gujarat and also in the neighbouring states of Rajastan and Maharastra. He could measure an elephant just by looking at it. It took him more than a month to make one outfit and as elephants need more than ten times the fabric we do it is an expensive business. Whenever one arrived for a fitting a gaggle of village children would form, endlessly fascinated by its sheer size.

With Mimi's costume Uncle Elephant had excelled himself. She wore a sequinned pink silk drape dotted with pink and white lotus flowers floating in an azure sea, which sparkled in the sun due to tiny gem-like stones embedded in the cloth. A couple of whales and dozens of exquisite rainbow fish were swimming in the swirling waters. She looked as if she were carrying the Arabian Sea on her back.

Mimi was the wedding transport for my cousin Ummi. Urmila Jivanhabi Patel, was about to become Urmila Rajeshkumar Patel. Ummi was a 'chisit', a Leicester girl with the broadest of accents. 'Chisits' are named for the way they inquire about prices, as in 'Emma Chisit?' ('How much is it?') She and I shared a love of the local dialect and voted 'Ooh, you booggarootah' our favourite phrase. We weren't sure what it meant other than it was an expression of shock and awe. Ummi was twenty and wasn't ashamed of being a fan of the local pop group, Showaddywaddy. Raj was twenty-one and favoured Bollywood hits, Ravi Shankar and classical sitar. Ummi was about to be led down the bridal path because fifteen months ago her parents had found out that she had a boyfriend. They were furious and the recriminations lasted for months. At one point Ummi asked me if she should run away but knew deep down that family ties were too close and she would marry a boy of her parents' choice.

I had never met Raj and Ummi had only seen him a couple of times the year before, when her parents brought her to Ganeshgam to find a husband. Her fearsome grandmother, Manjuma, had lined up half a dozen Patels. She was taking no chances: the bigger the choice, the more chance Ummi would find someone she liked. A quick glance through the black and white photos ruled out all but two of the candidates.

'There were some right horrors: bad teeth, bad hair; one looked like the village idiot,' she confided. 'I couldn't believe that because they were

'Patels from good families' she'd think I'd have any of that lot. There are limits.'

A quick-fire question and answer session eliminated one of the two remaining suitors on the grounds of education. Ummi was a university girl and she wanted a university boy. That left Raj, who attended Rajkot University where he was studying to become an engineer. She met him with a chaperone and he treated her to a *Thums Up* and a *kulfi* in a café. It wasn't love at first sight but there was a connection and he was funny, bright and - according to Ummi - very handsome. Handsome or not, the *Thums Up* was not a good portent. I would have walked out.

It was only a two-minute amble down the road to Ummi's family home but the journey was not straightforward. The most common obstacles were low-lying cows chewing the hay provided by locals. To leave them hungry would be a great sin as they are the holiest of all animals, the favourites of *Krishna* and revered because they provide nourishment in the form of milk. There were also several wild boars, a camel and a couple of bullock carts left unattended. Add the potholes and the newly-formed patches of mud and the short stroll transformed into a hazardous scramble. In addition, a number of guests were arriving on rickshaws from neighbouring villages, coming along the main road and down the slope. Their honking horns warned us to dodge out the way. A four-seater sped past carrying ten, most with their bottoms splayed outwards as they perched with their feet half-inside and half-outside, hanging on to the roof for dear life.

I once read about a court case involving a twelve-seater rickshaw in Hyderabad which had forty-six passengers. The judge told the driver he was free to go on two conditions: first that he would never do it again or he'd be jailed and secondly that he should return the following morning to demonstrate how he had fitted so many people into such a small space. This the driver did and the case was dismissed.

The dusty road fluttered with silk *saris* of every hue but red, which is always reserved for the bride. The stunning array was broken by men dressed mostly in dun and grey Nehru suits, although I noticed a few in western clothes with ill-fitting but fashionable flared trousers. One had forgotten to remove the Burton's Menswear label stapled to the back pocket of his hideous orange crimplene trousers. Displayed clearly in red was their price, £9.99, which would have bought him two much better, made-to-measure Nehru suits and a meal out in Munsari.

Outside Ummi's family home was an enormous banyan tree with aerial roots hanging down in a circle, giving the appearance of an open-air room. For the wedding it had been trimmed and shaped to resemble an umbrella. Sheltering underneath, crouched like old crones from a fairytale, was a distinct group in plain white *saris*, each one displaying gap teeth or no teeth at all. They were mainly the old women from the *poppadum* party with a few additions who had turned up in the same attire, wielding the same crooked sticks. They had reached the stage at which they could renounce fashion and not give a damn. 'Woe, woe and thrice woe,' I thought; 'toil and tedium: the wedding is about to begin.'

By the side of the banyan tree pavilion Mimi was chomping happily on a bowlful of bananas and papaya. Behind her was a huge pile of fresh dung and in it was embedded a whole papaya which had completed its journey up the trunk and through her middle and emerged unscathed and ready to eat again, if anyone cared to extract it from among the giant droppings.

Around five hundred guests had been invited. 'No other nation has as many relatives as Indians,' maintained *Bapuji*. 'Travel to New Zealand or Canada and meet a Patel and he or she will tell you they're related to your second cousin's wife's third cousin's uncle or aunt and suddenly they are part of your family, though you can't work out how. *Ba* and Bhulima understand it but it's a mystery to me, the maths is too complex. And they all have to be invited to the wedding or they take lifelong offence.'

The ceremony would take place in an elaborately decorated *mandap,* or canopy, with four giant pillars and silk drapes. As it was monsoon season it had been erected inside an enormous tent, where Ummi and Raj were being lectured on the order of service by the earnest *Brahmin*. When he finished I walked over and Ummi introduced me to Raj. He was affable with an easy and cheery demeanour and I immediately liked him. I could see why Ummi had accepted him, but still couldn't visualise marrying a virtual stranger myself. I tried to put the impending moment of truth with Bhulima out of my mind.

Conversation was difficult as the hubbub of guttural Gujarati voices drowned out almost everything but the *Brahmin*, who was now stridently chanting pre-wedding rituals in Sanskrit. For the bride and groom the wedding day is a marathon and once inside the *mandap* there is no respite for almost seven hours. I was certain I could not sit or stand for all that time, yet another reason not to cave into Bhulima's demands and end up with a lovely Hindu bride. Ummi and Raj were now surrounded by coconuts, garlands, rice, flowers and other necessary paraphernalia. Ummi looked so different in her red and white sari, shorn of her usual T-shirt and jeans: less tomboy, more Bollywood. I expected her to break into song at any moment. Raj was more modestly dressed, in a royal blue *kafni* with embroidered gold and red sleeves and an ivory silk *pijamo,* but his jaunty emerald turban gave him a princely air. A fierce wood fire stoked with *ghee* was making alarming fizzing noises as the couple circled around it. Men and women sat separately. Irritation welled inside me at this unnecessary division, but we were following centuries of tradition and everyone looked genuinely happy; especially Bhulima. She looked back in my direction, stood up and made straight for me, announcing her arrival with her deep signature belch. Then she sighed deeply as she lowered herself by my side and my heart began beating faster. I was sure everyone nearby could hear the thump-thump. Was she about to ask when I wanted to get married? I had prepared the reasons why I wasn't *quite* ready yet and rehearsed them in my head. She turned instead to Mukunddada, an old family friend and, of course, distantly related. She had always preferred the company of men. If any other woman had visited our men-only section eyebrows would have lifted, but Bhulima was unofficial Head Woman of the village.

Mukunddada's lips were stained red from the syrup in the *paans* he constantly chewed. *Paans* are betel leaves stuffed with fennel, *sopari,* aniseed, coconut and other spices, designed to improve digestion after a meal. Mukunddada chewed all day, as with gum. I heard he put tobacco inside his *paans* and that they were a cigarette substitute. He had a huge gap in his front teeth through which he was able to spit accurately at great distances without warning or apology. Apart from me, nobody seemed perturbed. The east has much to teach the west, but not this, surely.

'Do you remember when I got married?' Bhulima asked him. 'You must have been five years old and I was three.' He nodded, chewing furiously.

'You were *three* when you married Morardada?' I said.

'Yes. My mother was even younger. She was two. It was quite usual then. They sat me on my father's lap, put Morardada on his father's lap and we had a full ceremony. Everyone was invited and half the village came. Our family gave all the poor a jug of milk from our dairy to mark the day and also a mango. Of course, I don't remember a thing about it. They didn't tell me I was married, but Morardada and his family were always round at our place  and I was sent to Ganeshgam to help on his family's farm. Then when I was sixteen my mother took me to one side and told me I was married and we had another ceremony. It was just a continuation of my life, but also a new beginning. I was so excited and we were so, so, so happy.'

'But what if you'd hated him?'

'You have to trust your parents and grandparents. They have so much more wisdom than you. What does a sixteen-year-old girl know? Nothing! Experience and wisdom mean parents make the right choice. Morardada was the most wonderful man!'

I wasn't convinced. I knew that my uncle, *Bapuji's* younger brother, had divorced. 'What about *Nana?* His marriage didn't work out.'

'That is very rare, but it happens. His wife was the right choice at the time and a beautiful girl, but there were problems. She left a wonderful son and now we have found another lovely wife for your uncle and he could not be happier. Your parents are very happy, we were very happy. Your sister Kumud is so happy and already she is expecting her first child. And you will be happy. Very happy. You'll see.'

'Were you and Morardada always happy?'

'Always. It's such a shame he died before you were born. He would have been so proud of you and your sister and your many cousin brothers.'

'What did he die of?'

'Tuberculosis. But really it was the *gunda* British who killed him.'

'The British? How?'

Before she could answer she was called away to attend to the catering. She was after all the unofficial Village Head Taster and they wanted to make sure she approved of the fare before serving it to the multitude.

# Chapter 6

## The jailing of Morardada

**M**y mind abhors the unexplained. How had Morardada died? Why would the British kill my grandfather? What could he have done? I had so many questions, but Mukunddada was reluctant to answer them and I had to wait until the wedding was over. Hours passed: monotony interspersed with short irritating conversations about England. Was I looking forward to my own marriage? *Very much, thank you.* I hoped my smile was convincing. I wanted to snarl.

Eventually Mukunddada indicated that the end was nigh and I joined the crowd at the *mandap* listening to Sanskrit incantations I struggled to understand. After taking the seven sacred oaths Ummi and Raj were circling the fire with their clothes tied together and finally, to their relief and mine, they were declared husband and wife. I was starving and at last we could eat; but only after another ritual. Nobody had brought the bride and groom a gift. Instead they brought money, lots of it. Each sum had to be an odd number; otherwise bad luck, evil, the plague and death would befall them. A thousand rupees became a thousand and one, and so on. I noticed payments in American, Canadian and Australian dollars and even some Japanese yen. The Patel diaspora was conquering the world.

Once the cash was collected and logged in a book we were all ushered into the immense back garden. The dining area was flat and barren and at the back was a small wood, which I remembered as being full of strange noises from unseen creatures lurking in the foliage. There were no tables, plates or crockery. The men ate first. We were each given a huge banana leaf and the banquet was slopped on, almost as if we were in prison. But the end result was spectacular; a work of art. Everyone sat on the uneven ground on red cotton sheets, legs crossed yoga-style. I would have found the posture difficult, if not impossible, so was delighted, as a close relative, to be given a seat at the only table. Ummi was allowed to join us, despite being of the wrong sex: one of the privileges of a new bride. If it hadn't been the custom she would have insisted anyway and I doubted anyone would have been able to stop her.

We received three dollops of vivid vegetable curries. There was a potato and aubergine *shaak,* deep yellow due to the turmeric, a bright orange *lilva* with tomato sauce and a green and brown dish of black-eyed beans and tamarind with *methi.* For *farsan* we had glistening yellow *dhoklas* dotted with black mustard seeds and luminous green coriander. I was delighted to see my favourites on the menu: *banana bhajia,* begging to be dipped into a sauce of chilli, mint and tamarind. Next to them lay piles of *pooris* and vegetable rice and broken coloured *poppadums* completed the spread. Would any *maharajah* be dining better? I thought not and soon a cacophony of delighted belches would confirm it. As a converted westerner I tried to keep my emissions quiet and dignified. I was embarrassed when *Bapuji* and other older relatives loudly and openly gratified their post-prandial urges. Now I was in India I realised that there is a deep joy in showing you enjoy a meal and the west is poorer for its repressive politeness. *Bapuji* told me he had witnessed a *maharajah* belch so loudly after eating an exquisitely-spiced *pau bhaji* it could he heard across the vast sands of Chowpatty Beach in Mumbai. There was no embarrassment; rather it was an expression of the deepest satisfaction. The Queen, I decided, was unlikely to follow suit and would never experience the *maharajah's* happiness. Perhaps her constant restraint accounted for her miserable demeanour. Any semblance of a smile looked forced, except when she was gambling on her own horses and winning.

I had never lost the habit of eating with my hands, despite becoming accustomed to knives, forks and spoons. Like everyone else I began with the *farsan* then scooped *shaak* and a touch of lime pickle into a torn-off section of *poori,* dipped it all into the *khadi* or the *raita* and popped it into my mouth. In this way you can enjoy differing flavours and textures with every mouthful and add the satisfying crunch of the *poppadums.* Once the *pooris* were gone we mixed everything left into the rice. When we finished we waited for the servants to bring pitchers of water so we could wash our hands. The water splashed into the ground, the banana leaves were tossed into the compost pile and leftovers were fed to the birds, so there was no waste. I wondered how a jay or parakeet would react to a hot chilli.

The meal was the highlight and tedium resumed as the last formalities played out. I was delighted for Ummi. She looked genuinely happy, spending much of the day wreathed in smiles, but I knew that if I followed her I would be utterly miserable. The idea of marrying someone I had barely met horrified me. *Ba* and *Bapuji* were soulmates and so were all my aunts and uncles. We were all very close, constantly in each others' homes and such warmth would be impossible to fake. A system bringing harmony to so many couples has its merits. In the west so-called love matches often end in acrimony and divorce. Yet the feeling persisted that I had the right to choose. I might make a monumental mistake, but it would be my mistake. Convincing my family would be difficult; probably impossible.

At around six o'clock, just as a crimson sun was setting, the guests began to leave, but there was no welcome calming of the atmosphere. To be silent and alone is anathema to Gujaratis and the hullabaloo continued as we wandered home. I wondered whether the word 'contemplation' exists in Gujarati. It was certainly absent from our family's lexicon. A number of relatives and friends came back with us and noisily settled down with cups of *masala* tea. There was a lot of shouting and raised voices, steady state for us. I remember an English university friend arriving at our house in Leicester and asking whether we were having a row and should he stay outside. I laughed and explained that we always sounded as if we were at each other's throats due to our distinctive guttural accent.

'So what are you all talking about?'

'We were just having a laugh about how my Dad got drunk on his first Christmas in England and kept repeating a jumble of African words we couldn't understand.'

At dusk the cricket chorus was in especially strident voice, as if it were joining in the celebrations. We had acquired the leftovers from the festivities and by my reckoning would be enjoying wedding dishes for another two days at least. It felt odd to drink no alcohol, but everyone except me seemed relaxed and in no need of stimulants.

At breakfast next morning I decided to avoid negotiations about my future wife by centring the conversation on Morardada. I wanted to know the whole story.

'Morardada was the head man of the village, even at an early age,' Bhulima said. 'He was only twenty-two when his father died and he took over his mantle. At the very beginning he joined the Congress Party and was fully committed to Gandhiji's cause of independence for India. One night he called the whole village together and everyone supported self-rule. He was asked to go to meetings in Ahmedabad, Surat, Munsari and many other places. He was so eloquent; I was so proud. He would hold the audience spellbound. It was a gift he had.

'He spoke in front of large crowds and sometimes we'd see the British there, watching, taking notes; but they never said or did anything for years. It all changed after Gandhiji came here in 1936 and visited several villages. He...'

'He came to Haripur when I was four years old,' *Ba* interrupted her. 'Even then I knew he was a great man, although I did not understand the politics. His name cropped up in our conversations every day. Gangama took me to the rally, even though it was ten miles away and we had to go on a bullock cart. We set off at first light and when we got there she pushed and jostled with her elbows until we got right to the front of the crowd. She had amazing determination for such a tiny woman. She made me bow before Gandhiji and he put his hand on my head like this' - she broke off show the exact point at the back of her bowed head - 'and gave me his blessing. Gangama was so excited and for months afterwards she told everyone she met that *Bapu* had laid his hands upon her daughter's head.'

'So you met Gandhiji and never told me?' I was astonished. How could she keep that to herself? My father and mother had links to the greatest-ever Indian!

'I don't know why. It was a great honour but we try not to think of those times, because of what happened afterwards.'

Bhulima was impatient to continue her story, yet as she resumed I could tell she found it a struggle. Her eyes were welling with tears.

'After Gandhiji's visit the *gorias* warned Morardada to stop. They said he was a rabble-rouser. He saw their threats as a restraint on free speech so he took no notice.' Her prejudice was unrestrained: *gorias* is an insulting term for white people, in this case the British.

'The tipping point was when an Indian flag was flown on that banyan tree outside.' She pointed through the window bars. 'Someone had put grease all the way up the trunk so it would be almost impossible to climb up and take it down. They came here and told Morardada to bring it down at once, but he said it was nothing to do with him. So the *gorias* ordered a *doobra* to get the flag; but he kept sliding down, it was so slippery. We all laughed - it was really comical. But suddenly the atmosphere changed and they began to hit the poor *doobra* with *lathis*. He was screaming but they kept striking him.

'They were a dozen of them, all armed: eleven *gorias* and one Sikh soldier. Morarada tried to stop them hitting the *doobra* so they turned on him, hitting him with rifle butts and knocking him to the ground. I ran to him, but they hit me too. One *goria* spoke in broken Hindi but got his words mixed up and when he saw that Morardada didn't understand he shouted in English. '*Bapuji,* of course, could speak English very well because we'd sent him to Munsari for his education, and said they were screaming 'troublemaker' and 'traitor'. Poor Morardada was surrounded by yelling *gorias* and he was totally confused, you could see it in his face. He had no idea what they were saying and that made them even angrier. If he tried to speak they hit him harder.'

Tears were streaming down her face but I could feel her pride and admiration in every word.

'They put him in handcuffs and took him away. The Sikh, who was a kind man, gave me a letter written in Gujarati which was full of nonsense about Morardada being an enemy of the King and the Empire and a danger to the public. He said they would hold him in Rajkot jail. They knew before they came that they were going to arrest him - the letter proved it. They needed an excuse and I think they would have taken him even if he had brought down the flag. The Sikh whispered that he admired Morardada and hoped he would soon be home. He said he was sorry, but the *gorias* were afraid of people like him. He promised to come back soon to tell me when we could visit him in jail.'

'Was there a trial?' I asked.

'No. He was a threat, so they wanted him out of the way. They held him for six months as a political prisoner, guilty without any charge. It could have been worse. We found out later that political prisoners were taken to the Andaman Islands and the conditions in those jails were simply atrocious. It was a death sentence: very few returned.

'Mukunddada went to visit him in Rajkot. He said it was no place for a woman and it was best if he went alone. *Bapuji* wanted to go, but Mukunddada said he was too young. When Mukunddada came back he didn't want to tell me anything, but I made him promise to tell me the truth. I said I was not naïve. I knew it must be brutal, but it was better to know what it was really like than let my imagination run riot.

'What he told me broke my heart. He said there was blood everywhere and they never cleaned it up. The prisoners had to work in the baking sun all day, pounding coconuts until they could scoop out the insides into giant buckets, and their hands were covered in blood from non-stop labour. Do you know why they made them smash up coconuts? They were not even used for food - they were made into fibre for clothes.

'Morardada was strong enough to keep going but some of the men were weaker. One asked for water and a guard whipped him. I ask you, what sort of human being does that to another? But they will pay the price because *Shiva* never forgets misdemeanours, no matter when or how secretly they are committed. When they die they will all return as jackals or snakes, or worse.

'They were monsters, those *gorias*, sadistic. They were out to break the spirits of the freedom fighters, but they couldn't because they all swore to follow Gandhiji and refused to fight back or make trouble. Morardada said some tried to go on a hunger fast like Gandhiji, but they were force-fed and two died trying to resist.

'When Morardada came home he was so weak, so fragile. He hardly spoke for months. He didn't want to talk about what happened but his back was covered in bruises and weals. They had broken his body, but not his spirit.' Bhulima paused, unable to carry on.

'Now you see why we don't talk of those times,' said *Ba*. 'I think you should stop asking questions now.'

Bhulima wiped away her tears with her sari. 'No, he should know what went on. It was six months before Morardada was able to work on our farm again and he suddenly found a new strength as more and more joined Gandhiji's fight for freedom. It was as if *Rama* had given him vigour and courage. He began organising rallies again and hundreds and sometimes thousands would come and we'd hear everyone chanting '*Hindustan! Zindabad!*' over and over. It was hypnotic and it's a sound that echoes in my head whenever I think of him.'

Again she stopped and lowered her head into cupped hands as the memories flooded back.

'He was warned to stop. 'You cannot stop hundreds of millions of people,' he said, and after one more warning they arrested him again. This time it was much much worse. It was around *Diwali,* late in 1946, and he was held for six months. If Gandhiji had not become so influential by then I'm sure he would have died in jail. He wasn't just given hard labour: he was beaten, he was tortured. They wanted him to name everyone in the movement, but he stayed silent. Morardada said it made him more determined than ever to gain independence and that gave him the strength to survive.

'Then because independence was getting close, many political prisoners were released. We were so grateful to Gandhiji for this, but even so Morardada came home weaker than before. He could hardly stand. He looked old. He walked with a stick and his head was bowed, a little like Gandhiji's. But when independence came and the celebrations began he seemed to lose his stoop and his vigour came back. On Independence Day the government asked every town and village to raise the Indian flag and sing *Jaya Gana Mana* and Morardada was asked to organise it here.'

*Bapuji* had been silent all this time. 'I was sixteen years old on that day,' she said. 'It was Friday, August 15, 1947. As Head Man Morardada had the greatest honour of all: raising the Indian flag. But he was very modest, never one for fuss, and he asked me to do it. So we all gathered, every man, woman and child in the village, and I raised the flag. We sang '*Jana Gana Mana'* as loudly as we could and it was the proudest moment in all our lives. Morardada was crying openly but he kept telling me they were tears of joy and I should remember this day all my life. I looked around and many others were in tears too. It was like painting rainbows. We were overjoyed because we had our own government.'

'You raised the independence flag and never thought to tell me?'

'It's difficult. It's a time we want to forget. We were so proud of Morardada and so happy, but there was a price to pay. So many died during Partition. We were lucky, but in neighbouring villages Muslims and Hindus set fire to each others' homes and the wounds haven't healed. They never will, not for my generation. It was a war zone, a terrible time, and everyone knows someone who died for no reason, for no reason at all.

'In one small village the Muslims came at night and started killing people with knives and axes. They butchered them in their beds, even children and babies. Some managed to escape, but the Muslims found a group of men hiding inside a giant hollow tree and threw them all into a disused well, poured oil over them and set them on fire. In retaliation Hindus stopped a train packed with Muslims bound for Lahore. They set it ablaze and killed anyone trying to escape. These people lived side by side for centuries but Partition brought a madness no one can explain.'

I was appalled. I knew about Partition and the fighting as people moved in and out of newly-created Pakistan, but no history book I had read mentioned these atrocities. Back home, I had never grasped why Protestants and Catholics killed each other in Northern Ireland, or why they brought terror to towns and cities all over England. We had never mixed with Muslims but I made friends with some at university and no issue divided us, apart from our football teams. I suddenly remembered *Bapuji*'s mistrust of Muslims, his rants about the Pakistani cricket team and umpires cheating when they clearly were not. He had been scarred, unable to forgive or forget.

I turned to Bhulima. 'I thought you said the British killed Morardada. But he came home and lived for many years.'

'He lived five more years, but he was never the same. After independence he was a shell, forever coughing up blood and wheezing and most days he hardly got up. I barely had a conversation with him. He lay on the verandah watching people go by, half-asleep, half-awake, half-living, half-dead. Eventually he died of tuberculosis but I've always blamed the British, because he was such a strong man and he returned a ghost. Only now and again would we see the old Morardada.'

'Why did you go to England if the British killed your father?' I asked *Bapuji*.

'Before he died, Morardada told me to always look after the family. He said some Gujaratis were going to Africa and England and I should go too, for a better life. He said India was a great country but it would take many decades to reach its potential and there was a brighter future right now for those who take risks.

'He quoted Gandhiji, who said you should never hold grudges or look for revenge; that the weak can never forgive because forgiveness is an attribute of the strong. He had nothing against the British, despite what they had done to him. The time we fought for independence was over and we were at a new beginning. So when I went to England I never thought of the British as my enemies. The people I met there had nothing to do with the atrocities. I saw it as an opportunity, Morardada's fresh start. It was because of him we went to Africa and then England, so you could have the best education. I think he saw the future before any of us.'

We sat in silence until Bhulima declared the conversation closed by loudly belching.

'I am going to the toilet,' she announced. 'And when I come back you can look at the pictures of those beautiful girls I have found for you.'

# Chapter 7

## The unwanted bride and the snake charmer

The photographs were black and white, grubby and passport-sized, but Bhulima had a good eye for female beauty. She had scoured southern Gujarat in search for the very best bride for her grandson and was pleased with her efforts. She beamed from ear to ear as she produced the pictures from deep inside her sari with a magician's flourish

Each one displayed a Patel of the *Patidar* caste. I considered all Patels to be alike, but in Bhulima's mind there were important sub-divisions. Her aim was to match me with a Patel of equal standing; no more, no less. There was no question that I could marry someone from another cast and moving down the caste ladder would incur her wrath. Choosing someone above my station, like a *Brahmin*, would cause ructions with the bride's family. The main criteria were that my bride should be from a respectable *Patidar* family and be unrelated. The choices before me came with the endorsement of the formidable woman who was expertly dealing the photos onto a table, like a pack of cards.

All the girls were pretty, but one stood out. With her lustrous black hair, big sparkling brown eyes, teeth untainted by the usual addiction to sugary *pendas* and exquisite nose, she was the most beautiful girl I had ever seen. I had only the head and top half of her torso to go on and assumed the rest of her body would be in proportion. As my eyes settled on hers, Bhulima's smile grew as wide as the Ganges. She moved in for the kill.

'That is Anita, my number one choice. She comes from an excellent family and she is so modern-looking, not at all prim and old-fashioned like so many girls around here and she is very modest and polite. She comes most highly recommended.'

The treasure before me was extremely tempting and I hesitated; but for no more than a few seconds. For as long as I could remember, I had vowed to choose someone I had met and wanted to marry. I would have no one foisted on me, however enticing she might be. I had been preparing my excuses for years and now was the moment to produce them.

'She looks very nice, very nice indeed. But I am still studying. I've finished my degree but I'm going to do a postgraduate course in journalism and that will take a year, maybe two and I won't be earning anything. I really think it's best to wait until I finish my studies and get a job.'

'You don't need to worry about that: she will wait as long as you want.'

'I don't think it's fair to make her wait. Also, I want to marry someone educated, so we have things in common.'

'She has a first-class degree in mathematics from Rajkot and she's training to be an accountant. She is most intelligent and very smart. Her family runs a textile business in Munsari. They have two factories and Anita's *Bapuji* says you can have the smaller one, if you marry his daughter. That is an offer you simply cannot refuse. It will make you financially independent, so you do not need to worry about waiting to earn good money. You can earn it now, without doing anything!'

'But I don't want to run a factory. I want to be a journalist and I want to live in England, not here.'

'The family will run the business in your absence. You and Anita will own it but you don't need to do anything. It will all be done for you.'

I was running out of arguments.

'I'm sure Anita would make a lovely wife, but having lived in England I think I'd feel more comfortable if I could find a wife there. After all, there are so many Patels there now and a wife who grew up in England like Ummi would have much more in common with me. It is very different.'

As soon as the words came out I knew this was not a convincing argument. I was battling centuries of tradition and Bhulima was unused to anyone saying no.

'Urmila has married a local boy and she is very happy. I think you will be too. You should at least meet Anita. You will be charmed by her. Then you can decide.'

I had one more card to play. 'I'm not sure that would be fair. I really, really don't want to be tied to a marriage before I start working. I'd like to concentrate on my studies and all this would affect my focus. Also, it would run against what is laid down in my *janmotri*.'

When I was seven years old *Bapuji* had taken me to a soothsayer in Zambia who had handwritten a horoscope, mapping out the rest of my life. One of his forecasts had been very specific about my marriage.

'What do you mean?'

I showed her a tattered and torn fourteen-year-old beige horoscope, with its red sketch of *Ganesh* surrounded by a rectangle of *swastikas*. Inside were a series of predictions scrawled in faded blue ink. Some of them had already come true, like the forecast that I would have to leave Africa and travel far away to get the best education, forcing us to move to England.

'Look, it says clearly here that I will choose my own partner and that I will either marry at the age of eighteen or at twenty-five. Well, it's too late for eighteen and twenty-five indicates I need to finish my studies first.'

Bhulima burst out laughing. 'They can sometimes get the age wrong, but it's not important. What you are misunderstanding is that everyone chooses their own partner. I did, *Bapuji* did, but I or your parents have to find some candidates first and then you can choose. That is what it means. It is written in all *janmotris*.'

*Bapuji* unexpectedly came to the rescue. 'If he feels that strongly about his studies we should defer it. He is still young. We can easily find a suitable girl in England. There are so many in London, Manchester, Coventry and even in Leicester. I can get Amratkaka to make enquiries as soon as we get back. He has many contacts.'

I was overcome with guilt. I knew that whomever Amratkaka identified as my spouse I would never marry her, no matter how wonderful she was. There was also the question of Amratkaka's eye for beauty, which was not as sharp as Bhulima's. He had recommended some very dubious brides for other members of our family. My mind was made up. I alone would decide upon my lifelong partner. There would be arguments, followed by a rift; but I was prepared for that. I was certain that my family would finally support me, rather than throw me out. That was a battle for another day. Bhulima looked distraught but I was in no mood to give in now I had a reprieve.

'Yes, that seems like a good idea. I really need no distractions when I go to Cardiff University. It's a new place, a difficult course and I will have to work very hard. It will be hard to do that if I have other things on my mind. It would be a shame if I didn't achieve the highest marks possible and get the best job. I want to earn my own money, not rely on someone else. It's very important to me.' Even as I spoke I realised how pompous I sounded but fortunately it is the kind of language which resonates with my family.

'I suppose a year or so is not long to wait. But Anita's family will be very disappointed and she is such a good match. It is a shame. She is perfect in every way.'

'Who is perfect in every way?' Ummi entered though the front door. '*Jaisi Krishna.*' She placed her hands together and bowed her head slightly to Bhulima and my parents. Apart from greetings, there were no formalities in Ganeshgam. The doors were always open and no one ever knocked.

'Most definitely not this tiresome boy.' Bhulima pointed at me, but she was smiling so the danger had passed. 'I've found him a beautiful girl, so wonderful in *every* way, but he wants to put off his marriage until he has finished all his studies. Tell him how wonderful marriage is; make him change his mind.'

'It is wonderful and I can't wait to meet your future wife. I'm sure Bhulima will find someone sensational.' Ummi was teasing me: she knew that my resistance to an arranged marriage would be far stronger than hers. She once said that had she been male, she would have had a much greater chance of winning the battle against her family. She had capitulated, but only just. For all Patels family is paramount and most arranged marriages end happily, but I had an intuition that mine would not. Something indefinable kept me from the traditional path.

'Are you free today? Raj's friend Sunil has come to see us and we're off to the big city, Munsari, to do a bit of shopping and have *farsan* and *kulfi*. Would you like to join us?'

I most definitely would. I was desperate to escape the marriage inquisition. An hour later I was picked up by rickshaw and introduced to Sunil, who, as was traditional, worked on his family farm. They had acres of paddy fields and grew mangoes and he clearly loved his job. He was tall, with the obligatory Ganeshgam moustache and an earnest face and he spoke with great affection about those who worked under him. He was knowledgeable about modern farming methods destroying flora and fauna and wanted to know which chemicals we used in England; but I was the wrong person to ask. For the umpteenth time I wondered why nobody ever asked me how the thirteenth century Middle High German of Walter von der Vogelweide developed into the modern language, whether Goethe was a better playwright than Schiller or why Fyodor Dostoevsky was the greatest-ever psychological novelist. I was full of knowledge, but none of it seemed to be in demand.

I caught up on the newlyweds' latest news. There was to be no immediate honeymoon as they had decided to wait until Raj got his visa. Once it arrived they planned to tour Scotland. Raj had always wanted to visit the Himalayas and had heard that the Highlands are similar.

The road to Munsari was filled with perils and the deafening blare of out-of-tune klaxons. Many vehicles carried the invitation 'Horn Please' at the rear and horns were gleefully honked at by everyone overtaking. Our rickshaw darted between cars and lorries, avoiding them by the tiniest of margins, lurching its passengers wildly left, right, forwards, backwards and occasionally, when the manoeuvre was particularly daring, diagonally. Ummi had worked out an itinerary.

'We'll head for the market first because I want to buy some *saris* and Raj needs a cricket bat. Then we can eat and Sunil has an interesting plan for the afternoon. He's taking us to a leper colony.'

'A leper colony? Isn't that dangerous? Isn't it catching?'

'No, no, no,' said Sunil. 'It's not possible to catch leprosy unless you are in close contact for many months. Two of the lepers are old *doobras* who used to work on our farm and we have been helping them settle in. They have been in our family for generations and they are such nice people. The colony is a most interesting place. The people are extremely forbearing and never complain. It is most, most humbling.'

As we approached Munsari familiar music could be heard drifting across the plains: the unmistakable come-hither tune of a snake charmer's *pungi*. I asked the rickshaw *wallah* to stop. He was incredulous.

'This is not a good place, sahib. These are all liars, thieves and beggars and they are after one thing only and that is your money.' I insisted, because I wanted to take a picture and Ummi was equally keen. Raj and Sunil were dumbfounded.

The charmer wore a lurid orange *dhoti* and matching turban with a crimson ribbon hanging jauntily off one side. He had bulbous yellow and red beads and jade earrings dotted with tiny silver diamonds, long straggly grey hair, a white pointed beard and he sat cross-legged on a woven green mat. As he played his *pungi,* the cobra moved from side to side as if it were listening intently and dancing. I'd always assumed the instrument was a metal flute, but close up I could see it was made from natural materials. Two bamboo pipes were channelled into the top and bottom of a globular gourd, I guessed a pumpkin from its faded orange tint. As Ummi and I pulled out our cameras a small wiry man in a dirty *dhoti* blocked our line of vision. He was vigorously chewing a *kimam paan* and I could smell the tobacco. It was his way of feeding his nicotine habit, one which would almost certainly lead to mouth cancer, but he had more immediate concerns. His lips formed a circle and he expertly spat blood-red betel juice in an arc over my left shoulder, missing me by inches. As he did so he displayed daffodil-yellow teeth and a scarlet tongue.

'No money, no picture *sahib*.'

'How much?'

'Fifty rupees.'

Our rickshaw *wallah* stepped between us.

'Five rupees. No more.'

'Ten.'

'*Achha*, give him ten *sahib*.'

'How does he know the cobra won't bite?' I asked Sunil, but he had no idea. He repeated the question to the charmer's accomplice.

'Oh, no danger of that, *sahib,* we are removing his venom glands so he is being completely harmless. Other snake charmers are sewing up the snake's mouth, but then they are dying because they cannot be eating. We are not doing that because then you are needing too many snakes. This way, snake is being very happy, we are happy, everybody is happy.'

'How do you catch them?'

'People are calling upon us as soon as any snakes are coming into the house. The government is saying nearly fifty thousand people are snake-bitten and dying every year, so we are being very important. We are catching them with much courage, using sticks and sacks and we are saving many lives.

'Once we are catching a snake and the next day the family is calling us back in a big panic. The snake is leaving fifty babies in the house and they are crawling all over. It is taking us many hours to find them all but eventually we are rounding them up. More than eight generations of our family have been doing this vital work and, thanks to *Krishna,* not once are we getting hurt. We are world champion snake catchers; the best.'

'I read that the government has banned snake charming. Aren't you taking a risk on an open road like this?'

'No, no, no. The police are mostly looking the other way. Sometimes they are a nuisance but we are just running away. They are not chasing us because they need us when they are getting a snake in their own home. A snake is indiscriminate, it will even be going to a policeman's house. We pray to *Krishna* that they are especially choosing policemen and sometimes he sends them to police stations. If we are gone who will chase the snakes out? Also, we are carrying medicines for bites and many other ailments. We are snake doctors. How many people will be dying if people can't be coming to us, because they can't be affording to go to hospitals? The government is not thinking; they are all stupid. We are performing a vital service, vital.'

Ummi was fascinated by the swaying cobra, which had fully extended its hood. Its movements, smooth and hypnotic, were reminiscent of Kaa in the *Jungle Book* film, urging Mowgli to trust in him.

'The snake is dancing to the music. How do you teach it to dance?'

The wiry man chortled and spat out more red juice. This time the force and arc were greater and the result lay gently foaming on the dusty ground. I turned away, trying to hide my revulsion.

'No dancing, no dancing. Cobra is deaf, he has no ears. He is worrying the *pungi* will attack him, so he is being ready to strike back. He is following the *pungi* with his head, which is why it is also moving side to side. As you can well see, my brother Babu is sitting just out of range of a bite. The snake cannot be killing him with poison, but he still has his fangs and it is best not to be taking risks.'

Sunil and Raj were not interested in snake charming and growing restless so I gave the accomplice twenty rupees. He looked disappointed. He had been hoping for much more after volunteering so much information and I felt guilty. The money was nothing to me but it would probably buy him and his family food for the day.

We boarded the rickshaw and headed for the centre of Munsari where we were dropped off outside a dilapidated hospital next to the market. My tonsils were removed at a hospital here when I was four years old. I remembered coming home clutching a jar containing the tonsils, which the doctor had gifted to me. Was this the hospital? At the time it was reputed to be one of the most high tech in the Gujarat, but this ramshackle building looked to be the last resort of the desperate.

A poster advertising hydrocele surgery caught my eye: a poor drawing depicting a man staring in distress at what appeared to be a giant balloon, attached between his legs. A friend of mine, a medical student at Manchester University, spent six months at a hospital in Hyderabad as part of his training. He enjoyed regaling us with stories about the weird diseases which are common in India. Hydrocele, he said, is a condition in which a parasite enters a man's testicles and causes inflammation. Without antibiotics the area swells, sometimes massively. In rare cases the only way a man afflicted with this disease can move about is by carrying his testicles in a wheelbarrow. My friend showed us pictures of a man sitting cross-legged with a huge tray in front of him, apparently magically suspended in mid-air and covered in goods for sale. Closer examination showed it was balanced on his swollen scrotum.

There was a special offer of a hydrocele operation: a mere seven hundred rupees, which was about ten pounds. How safe the surgery was at that price, which would hopefully include a course of antibiotics, was anyone's guess. I felt a sudden sharp pain in my nether regions, lasting no more than a second or so and waved a hand in front of my trousers to ward off anything buzzing around, intent on damaging the most treasured part of my body.

A pungent smell suddenly hit us as an overweight woman emerged from the hospital. She hobbled over to the gates. She sighed, lowered herself gingerly onto a tree trunk lying by the road and lifted her sari to reveal her legs: one easily twice as wide as the other. She pressed her knobbly hands on the massive brawny limb, which resembled an elephant's leg but was uneven and pock-marked. It slowly oozed thick yellow pus and I turned away, disgusted. This was another condition: my friend had described: elephantiasis. He had spoken about its incurable nature and the hideous swelling caused by worms burrowed inside the body, but he had failed to mention the stench, which was akin to rotting meat. Ummi was staring open-mouthed, but Raj and Sunil were unfazed. What was riveting for us was banal to them. I was seized by the tourist's compunction to take a photograph, but resisted. The woman waved a copper begging vessel and both Ummi and I dropped rupees inside.

We had to jostle our way through the raucous market, which displayed a startling cornucopia. There were *saris* of every hue, material and value and tailor-made or off-the-peg shirts - or 'shirtings', as they were labelled in English. Stalls were brimming with men's *kurtas* and *lenghas*, puppets, jewellery, radios, hole-in-the-ground toilets, *charpoys,* mattresses, fruit and vegetables, blankets, chickens, wooden inlaid boxes, *pendas, samosas, pau bhaji, bhel puri* and other street food, leather slippers decorated with mirrors, home-made medicines guaranteed to cure anything and everything, spices, teas, gods made from wood, ivory and silver and an array of vividly coloured powders for the *Holi* festival. There were jugglers, clowns, dancers and dozens of beggars. Leicester Market boasts that is the largest and best covered market in Europe. Compared to this it was, as Bhulima would say, a fly on an elephant's backside.

Almost hidden by the throng was a small cul-de-sac where traders had discarded a small mountain of rotting food. Around twenty women and children were clambering about the slopes, sifting through rubbish and putting anything not crawling with maggots into plastic bags. I saw them collect a rotting cauliflower, battered guavas and bruised black bananas for their evening meal.

Ummi was inspecting *saris* so I followed Raj and Sunil into the cricket store. Raj made straight for a wall festooned with bats and played imaginary defensive strokes with half a dozen. Finally he settled on the one 'guaranteed to make you bat like the world's greatest cricketer, Sunil Gavaskar, hand-made from Kashmiri willow.' It was far cheaper and more solid than my mass-manufactured version.

We briefly escaped the searing heat in an air conditioned restaurant, where we ordered a selection of *farsan* and cold drinks. Ummi and I sighed with delight. The special mixed *chaat* was glorious and lived up to its billing as 'the crispiest, tangiest, spiciest, crunchiest, deliciousest snack in the world.' Our conversation turned to the blandness of English food.

'I would like to come and visit you all one day; but I couldn't eat boiled food without spices, like the English,' Sunil said.

'There are lots of Indian restaurants in Leicester now' I reassured him.

'But do they serve food like this?'

'There's only one in Leicester which has *pukka* Gujarati food and it doesn't compare. The rest do mainly meat curries but they're all based on Punjabi and Bangladeshi recipes. I read an interesting article recently about how Indian restaurants are changing the English diet. What you need to understand is that to make their food palatable the English pour something called gravy all over it. It's a brown sauce and quite bland, but they like it and they eat this sauce with almost every meal. Can you believe it? Anyway, a businessman went into a restaurant in London and ordered a chicken *tikka* with rice. Of course it comes out of the *tandoori* oven cooked in lots of Punjabi spices but it's a dry dish with no *masala* sauce. They offered him a coriander, chilli and garlic chutney but he said it was too spicy and asked the waiter for gravy.

'The chef had no idea what gravy was so the waiter said any sort of bland sauce would do and they opened a tin of tomato soup. The English eat many things out of tins. He put some cream in the soup and heated it up and the Englishman loved it. It's now a favourite English dish called Chicken *tikka masala*, or as we would say, nice chicken ruined by bland gravy.'

'Perhaps they should rename their country Blandland.' Sunil had dropped his serious air now that we were getting to know one another. Laughing at the eccentricities of the English diet we hailed a rickshaw to take us to the leper colony. We were visiting a place of suffering and yet I was looking forward to it. I was overcome by guilt.

# Chapter 8

## The leper colony

We bumped and bounced along an unmade road which seemed to be planted with stones and rocks. Our journey was observed by groups of black-faced monkeys enjoying a late lunch of orange persimmons. They screamed warnings from their treetop seats if we drove too close or if the rickshaw threw up red dust in their way.

The road lined with withered grey trees led up a small hill to the colony. Waiting for us at the bottom was a yellow and black cab which began moving as we approached. A hand appeared out of the rear window, signalling for us to follow. A makeshift gate with an orange flag marked the entrance. A lookout with the same crouching posture as the monkeys was stationed at the left post and as we began our climb he pointed animatedly at us and began shouting. At once we heard the first strains of a jolly tune, undoubtedly Indian but reminiscent of a sailor's ditty, inviting you to dance a jig even in your uncomfortable rickshaw seat.

Barely ten yards inside the gate a band was playing bells, whistles and flutes, standing in line and bookended by two *tabla* players. All the musicians were dressed in colourful rags, full of holes and tears. Behind them stood the entire colony, about two hundred strong, positioned as though for a group photograph. We staggered from the rickshaw, battered from our ride, to watch the show with the two occupants of the cab, better groomed and dressed than us. Their driver remained inside his vehicle, nonchalantly sipping a *Thums Up*. Ours leaned against a jacandara tree, his yellow-stained fingers holding a *bidi* which discharged a trail of vile-smelling smoke in our direction. Wisps hung in the still air.

The instruments could not have been easy to play because most of the performers' hands were missing one or more fingers. Some had lost an entire hand. One girl balanced her flute with two fingers on one hand and just a thumb on the other and played it beautifully, defying the laws of physics.

My knowledge of leprosy was based on the film *Ben Hur*, scheduled every Easter by the BBC. Judah Ben Hur, played by Charlton Heston, goes in search of his mother and sister and finds them in a leper colony, hideously deformed, and is so revolted that he doesn't reveal himself. The message is that leprosy is incurable and contagious and best avoided. In India many believe it represents divine retribution for sin.

The eldest of the band was a man in his sixties with a kindly wrinkled face and half a nose, the rest lost to leprosy. Parts of his ears were missing in an irregular jagged pattern, as if some creature had been nibbling at them. He had a full head of wiry white hair and a beard to match. He stepped forward and dropped to his knees, bowed his head and put one complete hand to the stump of the other in greeting. We all placed our palms together and mouthed a barely audible '*Jaisi Krishna*.'

Sunil introduced us. The old man was Sunil's servant, Jitandada, and he beckoned his tiny wife, Savitama, to step forward. Ummi and I winced as she hobbled towards us using a crooked stick a foot longer than herself. She had lost both most of one hand and an entire foot, but her smile was infectious. She was so delighted to see us it seemed churlish to feel embarrassed. She gave Sunil such a huge hug he had to prise himself away, so reluctant was she to let him go.

The men from the cab were a doctor from a local hospital, Nilesh Desai, and Ezekiel Punam, a Gujarati Christian who had established the colony a decade ago. They gave us a tour of the settlement, Ezekiel assuming the role of guide.

'Thank you so much for coming here. We appreciate it very much and, as you can see, so do the people here. It shows that the outside world cares and doesn't pretend they don't exist. They are spurned by many, whether educated or ignorant. We have the misfortune to have the largest number of lepers in the world, more than five million, and there is a presumption that they are reaping what they have sown; that they are being punished. Even many of the lepers believe that, but of course it is not true: it happens by chance and nobody deserves this.'

I asked whether leprosy could be cured.

'It is caused by a bacterial infection and treatments are available. They are not expensive, but the government will not fund them and people cannot afford them. So they are forced to beg, but of course people usually won't go near them. In spite of this they walk for two hours to Munsari and two hours back and return with little or nothing unless some kind soul is feeling generous. They cannot survive on the meagre amounts they get and nobody will give them jobs, not even the most menial ones, for fear of catching the disease. That is why we decided to set up this colony, to make sure they do not starve.' He put his arm around Nilesh's broad shoulders.' My friend here is good enough to come regularly to see if they need any treatment and we provide the money for any medicines. But, as Nilesh will tell you, if you mention the word 'lepers' people refuse to make a donation, which makes our job difficult.'

'That is true,' said Nilesh. 'Even some of my colleagues warned me not to come here, such is the ignorance. I am ashamed to say many of my family disapprove because they think the lepers are paying for the sins of their last life on earth. We must educate people, which is why we are always pleased to receive visitors. Only if you come here can you understand their suffering and begin to see that we need to do something about it. This is not one or two thousand years ago, this is today.'

Nilesh took Jitandada's withered arm and held up the stump so we could examine it. 'Jitan, his wife, his three sons, they all have leprosy. You see how jagged and rough this is? It's because when they sleeping outside at night the rats come and eat these numb affected parts. You could say there is no need for surgery because the rats do it. Of course Jitan feels nothing until the rat gets to the point where he still has feeling. For you and me, it's so horrific we can hardly believe it. Imagine waking up and being confronted by a rat eating you. It's like something from your American horror movies, but it's real.'

He released the arm more gently than he had lifted it, as if talking had released a pent-up anger, and pointed to some low-slung concrete blocks on the edge of the settlement.

'We house them there. You cannot stand up in those buildings but once you are inside and the door is shut the rats cannot attack you. Come, I will show you.'

We walked in silence. Nilesh pushed down the latch and leant on the door, which creaked open in the manner of a horror movie. We stooped and shuffled inside, bent almost double.

'You can see the beds because of the open door but watch what happens when I shut it.' Another creak and we were engulfed in total darkness. The heat intensified and I became claustrophobic and inclined to panic until Nilesh opened the door again, letting in not just light but air. 'You can't make out shapes so you have to feel for your bed. I always say it's like hell but it's a safe hell, not a home but a haven. We want to build something better, a home fit for habitation; but we need money and we don't have it.'

'Never listen to those who say you don't need money to be happy,' said Ezekiel. 'Those people either have enough or too much. These people have nothing. With money we could change all these lives and think how much happier they would all be. As it is, we can give them a paltry fifty rupees a month, which buys them rice and *dhal* and sometimes alcohol.' He smiled at our surprise. 'I know it's not meant for that but I say, the money I give you, you can purchase alcohol if you want. Their suffering is great and if they need the relief of alcohol to forget, who am I to deny them? They say to me that nobody cares and I tell them we care and, more importantly, God cares and God loves them and God will keep them safe.'

We trooped outside and I saw that Ummi's eyes were damp, her face contorted as she held back the tears. I felt numb, like the lepers: unable to feel sadness or pity or even to think because what we had learned was so shocking I couldn't take it in.

Jitandada and Sunil exchanged news about their families and the conversation moved on to the time Sunil had fallen into slurry during monsoon rains and Jitandada had rescued him and they both burst out laughing. Their snorts and cackles brought me back to myself, as if air had managed to penetrate a vacuum.

A sprawling neem tree towered over the blocks, casting a giant shadow around them. At the left side of its trunk Nilesh produced a white coat and a stethoscope from his briefcase and as soon as he put on his uniform a gaggle of more than twenty patients formed a patient untidy queue. He had brought a small supply of medicines which he prescribed to the neediest, free of charge. On the right side had Ezekiel set up his own surgery, dispensing fifty rupees to each family. The money and medicine were accepted with grace and humility; thanks dispensed by the coming together of hands and a nod of the head. Afterward, Savitama appeared with a tray of cardamom tea and water in plastic cups. Sunil had a warning for us: 'The water is from the well, so don't touch it. It may not agree with your delicate western stomachs. Of course we are used to it but I have seen Europeans suffer terribly after just a few sips. The tea is perfectly safe because the water has been boiled.'

'There is so much need in India,' said Nilesh, as we sipped the aromatic infusion. 'Sometimes it overwhelms you. All we can do is help someone here and there. We are like travellers on a beach: we pick up pebbles and we clean and polish them carefully. But we can't pick up every pebble or grain of sand and the rest have to fend for themselves.'

It was getting late and as we climbed into our vehicles the band struck up again, the catchy tune becoming an ear worm in my head all the way back to Ganeshgam.

# Chapter 9

## Pilgrimage to Shirdi

**T**he next morning Bhulima announced that we were going on a *jatra*. In India Gujarati families never go on a holiday: they disguise it as a pilgrimage. The experience always involves a shrine, prayer and generous almsgiving. It also involves a detour with sightseeing, shopping and plentiful *kulfis* on the menu. The equation is simple: penance at the shrine earns you the right to fun afterwards, but pleasure alone leads to damnation.

'This time was reserved for you to get to know your future wife,' said Bhulima darkly. 'Now that's not going to happen. We can see you are getting bored with village life, so this is a good time to go on a *jatra* so that we can do *darshan* in Shirdi.' She was peeved. Important as this trip was, it was definitely her second choice. 'It's essential that every member of the family goes to Shirdi at least once to receive a blessing so that we prosper in our future life.'

Each Hindu family venerates a particular god or spiritual leader, in the way that Catholics revere different saints. We were devotees of *Sai Baba*, a legacy passed down the generations, and Shirdi was the location of his *mandir*. *Sai Baba* was an *avatar* of *Shiva* and is worshipped by both Muslims and Hindus.

My parents often spoke about Shirdi. They told how Morardada and his father, Nagardada, before him had undertaken the difficult two hundred mile pilgrimage to Maharastra pray for the health and wellbeing of the family and how their wishes were always granted. Nagardada had walked there and back, an epic trip for a man fuelled only by rice, *dhal* and faith. Morardada's journey had been more leisurely, by train, horse and cart. They had both come straight back home, Nagardada in two months and Morardada in ten days. We were also visiting the seaside and the Himalayas, which I hoped would be more relaxing.

*Jatras* have become easier since the days of Morardada and Nagardada; although not for everyone. I shuddered as I recalled the experience of a *Brahmin* friend. Arun belongs to the highest caste and his father told him he would not be regarded as a proper *Brahmin* until he went through an initiation ceremony. Arun was keen to become an engineer and had no ambition to become a priest, so he protested. His father refused to listen and Arun was packed off to the Himalayas where, like a Baptist, he would be submerged in the waters of the holy River Ganges. After that he would spend a week caring for the poor in an *ashram*. His tasks, decreed by centuries of tradition, were to wash them, feed them and accompany them to the toilet if they needed assistance. As soon as he arrived Arun was given the holy rites, grasped by the ankles and immersed upside down in the Ganges. What he had not realised was how cold the Ganges is at this point as it gushes down from the Himalayas and the shock of the almost-freezing water knocked him unconscious for several hours. He did recover and went on to complete his duties to the poor, but his experience left him badly shaken.

Bapuji produced the giant map of India which he always carried neatly folded. It bore the title 'INDIA States and Union Territories' in bold letters and the states were easy to pick out because they were all in different pastel colours. He pointed to the pink zone bearing Maharashtra, Shirdi and Mumbai.

'Afterwards we will visit Mumbai and stay with Sumankaka and Minakaki. You loved it there when you were little. Then if we have time we'll take a train to the Heem-hal-hee-yass.' His pronunciation briefly confused me as he used his peculiar intonation. 'We will see. You can never be certain if the train will arrive today or tomorrow or not at all. Indian time is much more laid-back than English.'

We began our *jatra* by rickshaw to Munsari, where porters in brick-red shirts, black trousers and peaked blue and gold caps fought tigerishly for the right to carry our luggage. A scuffle was breaking out when *Bapuji* picked out a random porter and the others scuttled away seeking new prey.

Train journeys in England were mundane. British Rail provided uncomfortable seats in dull carriages on trains which were invariably late. The waiting rooms were poorly heated, the tea undrinkable, the food diabolical. Every excursion I could recall was as dreary as the grey clouds which inevitably lowered overhead. Arriving at an Indian railway station was like entering a firework display: a fizzing, vibrant and boisterous arena which completely overwhelmed me. The street outside and the wide station archway teemed with entertainers. There was a juggler, a *tabla* player, a mime artist and a woman with a soulful voice singing folk songs without accompaniment.

Two acts stood out. In front of main building a puppet show had attracted a sizeable audience of families with young children. The puppet master was a handsome man with a Maharajah moustache, dressed in traditional Rajastani red, green and yellow. The performance was macabre slapstick, fighting and arguments in silly voices. *Tablas* began playing and a puppet seized its own head with both hands, whipped it off like a hat and began to juggle it to shrieks of delight from the crowd. The eyes began rolling around in its head and one popped out, so the puppet stooped down and shoved it back in. Finally the torso and head were reunited and the puppet accepted the wild cheering and applause with vigorous salaams. Inside the archway an ungainly man was dancing to a *bhangra* beat with a black and white langur. Wispy hair looped out of his sapphire turban and he wore a red and yellow *dhoti* dotted with blue stars. His partner was similarly attired. The man's ungainly movements reminded me of *Bapuji's* bad dancing, his widespread arms moving up and down like an aeroplane in distress while his bottom half was still. Luckily for him all eyes were on the star turn, the lissom langur, a far more graceful mover and shaker who showed off his fearsome teeth with incessant chatter, delighted to be the centre of attention.

We left the side-shows and entered the main hallway, which was seething with hordes of passengers trying to buy tickets at just two windows. The walls reverberated with the discord of hot angry passengers shouting, screaming and screeching gutturally as only Gujaratis can. A space in the centre was occupied by four men sleeping contentedly, oblivious to the hullaballoo. We waited patiently for our turn until we reached a window and were confronted by an over-officious ticket seller. He glared at *Bapuji* through hideous horn-rimmed spectacles as he asked for four tickets to Shirdi.

'Have you made a prior booking?'

'No. Should I have done?'

'Most definitely, if you want first class. Do you have identification?'

Bhulima stepped in.

'Sudhir, ever since you were born you've been a nothing but a *kagro*. You give my son his tickets, show some respect and stop being so damned bureaucratic or I'll tell your father to sort you out once and for all.' *Kagro* was Bhulima's favourite insult. She hated crows. 'They don't do any work to get their food, they just steal anything left behind and they are as evil as *Ravana*.' Recognising Bhulima, Sudhir looked sheepish and issued the tickets.

'Here, four first class, the best we have available, Bhuliben.'

We made for our platform, which was even more crowded and noisy, our senses accosted by the sight and smell of food. Vendors had occupied the prime spots and were producing snacks on an industrial scale. Samosas, *kachoris* and onion, potato and banana *bhajias* were sizzling in dangerously positioned vats of hot oil. Beside them *pau bhaji, bhel puri* and *ghathia* stalls were doing a roaring trade. Children of around ten or younger were rushing around offering tea, their shrill voices echoing across the tracks as they chanted, '*Garam chai, chai garam.*'

As I paid for four *garam chais*, all with copious and obligatory sugar, I was almost knocked over by a man carrying a mattress. I stumbled and spilt half the contents of the plastic cups over my trousers and shoes. I span round to confront him, but he had already darted five yards ahead. He was dodging in and out of the melée, only occasionally damaging unsuspecting passengers. I thought he was a hunchback until it dawned on me that he had a suitcase strapped to his back. He was followed by an equally nimble family, his wife carrying two heavy chairs with ease and four children bearing a large black trunk, multi-coloured blankets and a table.

We settled into our carriage. Notices all round proclaimed it was first class, but I felt it was second at best. It was my first experience of luxury travel and I told *Bapuji* I was disappointed. The compartment was scruffy, the lights flickered and there was a stench of sweat and rotten vegetables, even though everyone looked clean and no one was carrying old cabbages.

'You have a seat, air conditioning, a bunk if you want a nap and a toilet you can actually use,' retorted Bapuji. 'So stop moaning.'

Bhulima told us Morardada had travelled third-class. The train was so full he had to sit on the roof for most of the journey alongside a man with a panic-stricken goat, which bleated continually and defecated regularly. The man had a pile of betel leaves in a sack and he used them to pick up the mess and throw it away. The next day Morardada recognised the plaintive bleating in Shirdi. He saw the same man tethering the distressed goat to a fence before entering the shrine, chewing a betel leaf.

Indian Railways were rolling out new diesel and electric locomotives, but ours was steam-powered. The black smoke billowed overhead as we chugged first to Mumbai and on to Shirdi. I poked my head out of the window and sniffed the air. I had always preferred the smell of steam to diesel and I savoured the heady combination of coal fire and hot oil. In the distance a row of five squatting men chatted animatedly at the edge of a bright green paddy field which lay under six inches of water. I thought they were resting until I noticed they were holding up their *dhotis,* happily relieving themselves in public view. The evacuation of bowels was just one of the entertainments. There was an ever-changing landscape of animals: wild and domesticated, large and small, ploughing, pulling carts, slumbering or fleeing. I watched armies of workers digging, chopping, planting and cutting. Whenever we passed a river or a lake, *dhobi wallahs* were busy thrashing clothes on the stones. I had brought a copy of McNae's *'Essential Law for Journalists'* to prepare for my return to university, but didn't open it. The delights of the expensive hardback were nothing to this vista.

Over the next ten hours we stopped more than a dozen times. Whenever the train pulled into a station it was as if a curtain opened on a new show. There were open fires on platforms for frying snacks and heating water for the *garam chai.* There was an ever-changing menu and heaps of fruit and we could buy whatever we wanted though the window, without leaving our seats. I remembered wandering through eight British Rail carriages to find the last curled-up cheese sandwich on sale: this was paradise. The finale was a spectacular cinnamon sunset and at last I opened the pages of McNae's classic law book, but within minutes found it tedious after the thrill of spotting elephants, camels and macaques flash by, so I dozed until the screeching of brakes announced that we were approaching Shirdi.

We spent the night at a hotel which looked dubious from the outside. The windows were boarded up and the 'Fust Class Suprim Hotel' sign was the only clue that it was a high-class establishment. The room rates were written on the side of a cardboard box resting on the reception desk. Bhulima was shocked at the extortionate charges. 'Why are you wasting your money?' she asked *Bapuji* with vehemence. 'One night here would buy us rice and *dhal* for a whole year.'

The Suprim Hotel proudly displayed three stars, but they were unearned and unjustified by the facilities. I was delighted to find a fridge in my room, but when I opened it there was an exodus of giant black ants, so I slammed it shut and the handle fell off. To my surprise there was a light on inside, but the fridge was not working as the colony had clearly been established for some time. I examined the bed and found stains on the sheets where my predecessors had been bitten by mosquitoes, leaving dozens of tiny blood spots. I wandered into the bathroom and was relieved to find a sit-down toilet, but sadly it refused to flush until I poured a whole bucket of water into the cistern. This was not easy as the water dribbled, hissed and exploded from the tap in fits and violent spurts. I tried the shower and watched a weak intermittent spray of discoloured water. In despair I returned to the room just in time to spot three cockroaches scuttling back under the bed. A flash of green scurried across the floor and climbed up the wall to settle upside down on the ceiling alongside two other lizards. Next to them and directly above the bed, a fan wobbled round unsteadily, filling me with the dread of decapitation while I slept. I grumbled to *Bapuji* about the state of my room. He was unsympathetic.

'It's not like you've got rats. A doctor once told me cockroaches mean that your room is clean, so they are a good sign. They are fastidious: you find them in many hospitals. The lizards are also good news because they will eat the insects and you are less likely to be bitten.'

'What about the toilet?'

'So you'd rather have a hole in the ground? You can still use it and it's better than squatting. You really have been spoiled by living in luxury in Leicester.'

Luxury? We lived in a small terraced house and there was mould on every wall of my bedroom. 'Have you every stayed anywhere as bad as this?'

'Trust me, this is opulent. I remember a place I stayed in when I first landed in Africa. I stopped at a hotel in a place called Mwunza in Tanzania in the middle of nowhere and was delighted when the receptionist said a room would cost a few shillings, less than fifty pence. Opening the door was like stepping into an oven and it was buzzing with flies, but otherwise it was empty. So I went back down and asked for a bed. That was another shilling. A couple of boys came up and threw a dirty mattress on the floor, so I went back down and asked for some sheets. He wanted another shilling. I was roasting in my room – you have a fan. I was tormented by insects, but you have lizards to protect you. As I said, opulent.'

I survived the night in my plush bedroom, undisturbed by my companions, and was wakened at dawn by Bhulima bawling her *puja* in an adjoining room. A red sun was rising fast through brindled clouds. We breakfasted on *fafra*, fried chillis and cups of *masala chai* laced with ginger and boarded a passing rickshaw. It was not seven o'clock but we were three hours late for the first *aarti* of the day at the *mandir*. We had discussed rising early but decided that we needed a full night's sleep. We were definitely not devoted pilgrims.

The streets were brimming with *Sai Baba* memorabilia. Hundreds of statues of the saint were on sale, mostly made of ivory, varying in size and wearing different outfits. No matter how rich or poor you were there was a *Sai Baba* just right for you. Bhulima told me that around fifty thousand people visit the shrine every day, many queuing through the night so they can take part in the first *aarti*. The next one was not until midday, but an excitable throng was on the move, drawn like slow-moving magnets by the allure of the saint. Their destination was an unlovely dung-coloured edifice given some magnificence by a gleaming gold dome and triangular orange flags. As we neared the shrine we could hear the bleating of bewildered goats, abandoned, as in Morardada's day, by pilgrims intent on fulfilling their own spiritual needs. One man was just leaving his goat and salaaming his way to the temple, deep in contemplation and oblivious to the pitiful cries behind him.

The surroundings were a mix of ugly concrete and ramshackle stalls selling knick-knacks. Vendors urged customers to buy plates, cups and towels covered with clumsily-sketched and coloured images of *Sai Baba*. Hindus are almost always cremated, but holy men are sometimes buried and Shirdi was the saint's resting place. I felt he would be uncomfortable in his grave if he knew about the cheap and extremely nasty goods cobbled together in his name.

It is only when you leave behind the hubbub of the baying vendors and snack-sellers and enter the complex that you realise a pearl has been hidden inside an unsightly gargantuan oyster. Outside, you despair of the disarray, hysteria and chaos humanity can create. Inside, man has created art inspired by a saint who taught Hindus, Sikhs, Muslims and Christians not to fight, but to live together in peace.

Piped music kept us entertained during an hour of queuing. The *mandir* was heaving with sweaty bodies intent on taking part in the *darshan,* which was underway. Centre stage was a statue of *Sai Baba* arrayed in a peacock blue *kafni*, gold *langot* and his traditional white cloth headgear. In front of him *Brahmins* clad in scarlet robes with saffron scarves were accepting personal items from the congregation to be blessed. To a musical accompaniment blaring from speakers they grabbed whatever was thrust into their hands, waved it briefly towards *Sai Baba* and within a second or two returned it to its owner. Everyone arrived with a perfectly ordinary book, hat or necklace and left bearing an article rendered holy. A handsome brown and cream monkey was enjoying the ceremony from a ledge to the right of the entrance, its mouth firmly shut and its hands joined, as if in prayer. Nobody tried to chase it out and it looked as entranced by the proceedings as anyone.

A deep and genuine reverence had overcome the bodies and souls of *Ba, Bapuji* and *Bhulima*. They appeared to be in some kind of trance, their faces showing a fervour and dedication I had never seen before. Their lips moved in silent prayer and their hands were firmly clasped below their quivering lips. I felt compelled to join in; but what should I pray for? Success for Leicester City seemed trite, so I opted for health and happiness for my family. A sudden panic gripped me as I realised that, apart from the clothes I was wearing, I had no object I could offer for a blessing. I put my hand in my pocket and pulled out the fixture list for next season. It would have to do: the results would demonstrate whether *Sai Baba*'s powers were still working. I hoped he liked a challenge.

We emerged blinking into the bright sunlight and completed our tour: the obligatory visit to the neem tree under which *Sai Baba* sat meditating for many years and the simple meal of chapatti, *gobi aloo, dhal* and rice in the giant hall, served as *prashad* to the rich and the poor. We sat in an enormous canteen with Formica tables and unsteady plastic chairs where the food was slopped out onto steel plates. Afterwards, *Bapuji* made a large donation to feed the poor and he, Bhulima and *Ba* fell again into silent prayer before another *Sai Baba* statue. I knew that the amount was substantial because the brown envelope he handed over was bulging at the seams. This was the moment to ask *Sai Baba* to grant wishes, but again my mind was unfocused on the task before me. Is it right to ask for something from gods and saints in return for money, especially when we could afford to hand it over without suffering any hardship?

A sudden long and deeply mournful belch from Bhulima marked the end of our worship.

# Chapter 10

## The dirty Himalayas

As soon as we stepped out of the *mandir* complex we effortlessly slid from the spiritual realm to the materialistic and began shopping for a *Sai Baba* statue. There were so many hideous versions available, yet I could not find a single one I wanted to buy. Bhulima's stern face told me that refusal was not an option, so I chose the smallest one she would allow. It would have to take pride of place in my room in front of my Leicester City poster and I could only hope that *Sai Baba's* good *karma* would inspire my erratic team to greater glories.

That night I was joined by an extra lizard and two more cockroaches and the following morning we caught the early train to Mumbai. The ever-changing vista though the window rarely failed to delight and my brand new copy of McNae remained pristine. Occasionally the view turned ugly as we passed squatting men openly defecating and towns and villages being modernised with sprawling concrete, but these scenes were invariably broken by a trumpeting elephant, a lively camel or a pack of boars rampaging through traffic. The women carrying goods and copper water urns on their heads fascinated me most. I had tried balancing my school bag filled with books on my head and ended up with a cricked neck and two days of pain; but they were nonchalant, moving with easy grace. *Bapuji* said some walked twenty miles a day just to bring water from the nearest well.

Apart from our arrival at the airport my last visit to Mumbai had been at the age of five and the memories were hazy. The train chugged in just as it was getting dark and we hailed a rickshaw. This time a statue of *Krishna* in front of the steering wheel, a fearsome cobra displaying red fangs wrapped around his neck, guaranteed safe passage to our accommodation on Chowpatty Beach. The rush-hour traffic was denser than anything I'd seen even in London but it moved faster, with lorries, cycles and scooters weaving in and out like dodgems. Cows wandered about as if they owned the roads and were in little danger as hitting them is a mortal sin. Pedestrians played Russian roulette by abruptly stepping into the road. Somehow they avoided the bullet, even when it seemed impossible.

On every street people were sleeping rough. I'd seen three or four in the centre of Leicester, but this was on a far larger scale. The pavements were overflowing with sprawling humanity, not just men and women but babies, the aged and infirm. Meals were being cooked on fires at the roadside and there were *charpoys* and chairs to furnish the open-air homes. There were no toilets, so these were definitely areas to avoid just after dawn. I glanced at my family and was hit by a sudden realisation. The traffic dodgers, the perilous roads, the poverty on the pavements, the defecating men, the cows roaming free, the tap water they drank without concern for their health, the enjoyment of loud belching after every meal, all these were commonplace to them, the routine of everyday life. To me they were alien, peculiar, outlandish. I was seeing everything with fresh eyes, amazed, excited and shocked. They had seen it before, many times. They belonged. I came from the same place as they did, felt a huge affinity with it; but I belonged elsewhere.

Sumankaka and Minakaki's ground floor apartment overlooking the Arabian Sea was much smaller than our house in Ganeshgam, but neater and more sophisticated. The living room and dining area resembled a museum, filled with oil paintings and watercolours, and were divided by a tiny fountain of *Krishna* playing his flute, the water springing out of it. There were no open fires, no pile of mangoes and the floors were covered with Kashmiri rugs. Despite all this the bathroom was very Indian, though slightly better-equipped than ours. There was a nicer, less putrid hole in the ground on one side and hot and cold water taps next to the bucket and jug on the other, so you could have a full body wash.

The sea was calling me but it would be rude to rush out, abandoning our hosts. I stepped on to a balcony overlooking the beach with its milling crowds and I breathed in deeply. I could smell the sea mingled with the herbs and spices being liberally scattered by food *wallahs* cooking everything from *samosas* to *pau bhaijis*. Another odour, less pleasant, hung in the air, but I couldn't work out what it was.

Sumankaka and Minakaki had remembered that my favourite meal was okra and *khadi* and that I also loved sticky *jalebis* and *shrikhand*. This was no longer true. The high sugar content of *jalebis* and *shrikhand* meant visits to the dentist and I'd weaned myself off them, but was too polite to say so. They were keen to hear my news. How were my studies going? How did Leicester and Manchester compare to Mumbai? Were they as big? Had I chosen a bride?

We spent a couple of days touring the city and saw all the famous sites: the Gateway of India, from where the last of the British troops departed, leaving behind an independent land; Marine Drive with its flaking art deco buildings; the Elephanta Caves and magnificent statues of *Shiva*; the Towers of Silence where vultures pick clean the dead bodies of Parsis and finally, to please *Bapuji*, the Wankhede Cricket Stadium. No one seemed interested in the attraction right in front of us, Chowpatty Beach, so I went alone for a stroll. 'Be careful,' warned Minakaki. 'It's full of pickpockets.'

It was dusk, when British beaches are almost deserted. Here, the multitudes were jostling for space with more arriving every minute. A few overhead lights, blazing fires and the *diwas* carried by groups performing impromptu *puja* produced a satisfying glow. Shadows moved constantly, the largest cast by a ferris wheel and a merry-go-round filled with squealing children. I was hit by the aroma of food of every description: coriander, garlic, chilli and mustard seed lingered everywhere and I sniffed them joyfully, like a dog. But my enjoyment was short-lived as the sudden stench of sewage made me choke, a full blast of the mystery smell I'd experienced on the balcony. Garbage and litter were everywhere too: I had removed my sandals and narrowly missed stepping on broken glass, so I hastily put them on again. I had wandered into a crazy outdoor party with at least half a dozen monkey acts and serial snake charmers. Hawkers were selling anything and everything: clothes, soap, perfumes, combs and every fifty yards there was another *paan* stall. The familiar Mumbai cuisine was here in force: *ragda petis, samosa chaat, Pani Puri, pau bhaji. Kulfi* sellers were doing brisk business and in the gloom cricket matches were being played and a talented artist had crafted a giant standing elephant out of sand, waving its trunk at a sandy Amber Palace. A group of tourists had brought along idols of *Ganesh*, which they blessed by sprinkling them gently with sea water before setting them next to a row of *diwa* lamps and bowing their heads in prayer.

'Please sir, please give me money. I am starving and so is my family. Please, please, please.' The girl was about ten years old. She had the biggest eyes I had ever seen and they were streaming with tears. She wore brightly-coloured rags full of holes and her hair was tied with a red ribbon, fluttering gaily in the breeze. She had lost an arm but the other was outstretched: she had instinctively spotted a foreigner on her patch. I may have looked Indian, but she saw a stranger. I pulled out ten rupees and gave them to her.

'This will not feed my family. We need more. Much more.'

So I gave her another ten and walked on. She followed, keeping pace alongside with her palm upturned, occasionally pawing at me with her bony hand.

'Please, please, please, sir, you have all the food you want. Twenty rupees is not enough. There are eight of us and my father is dead and my mother is crippled and my baby brothers and sisters have not eaten for days. Please, please, please, sir.'

'I'm sorry, that's all I have.'

Her beseeching never ceased and after a few hundred yards I rounded on her and asked her to leave me alone, but to no avail. I dived into a public toilet even though I did not want to use it and the overpowering stench soon drove me out. She was waiting patiently outside, so I dashed past her and sprinted as fast as I could, until I lost her. With the beach so crowded I was confident she would not find me again, so I stopped for a pistachio and almond *kulfi* and settled down on the sand to watch the Mumbaians at play, then walked slowly back towards the apartment, feeling much more relaxed. Ahead of me I saw the girl with the red ribbon accosting a tourist with a backpack.

'Please, sir, please give me money. I am starving and so is my family. Please, please, please.'

The following morning we ate *parathas* stuffed with potatoes, spinach and chillis accompanied by yoghurt, to prepare us for the long journey north. Minakaki told us the yoghurt originated from Ganeshgam and dated back half a century. Her mother had made it as a young woman and the remains of each batch were used to make the next. When her mother died she brought a pot with her to Mumbai and carried on the tradition. Bhulima said that her own yoghurt would have been even older, but it had been neglected and lost while she was on a *jatra* ten years ago. I told them that in England we bought yoghurts in plastic pots from supermarkets and they looked at me with pity. Who would waste hundreds of rupees on something that could be made for virtually nothing?

The Himalayas are a backdrop to hundreds if not thousands of Bollywood movies. After many difficulties and obstacles the hero and heroine find love and they sing and dance on the mountainside amid pink and yellow flowers and trees with snow white blossom. Everything is pristine, the air is wonderful and visitors return refreshed in mind and spirit. To reach this paradise we were undertaking a trip equivalent to travelling from London to Naples. This time the first class carriage was of a higher quality and the bunks more comfortable as I watched the ever-changing landscape fly past: the farmlands of the Gujarat, the deserts and palaces of Rajastan, the paddy fields of Haryana and the vast wheat pastures of Punjab. The journey took two days and we emerged from our carriage with tired minds and bowed bodies. It was only now that I discovered why we had made the odyssey. There was another temple, Bhulima informed me; yet more bouts of intense prayer and spiritual fervour just over the horizon.

'When Morardada was in jail he became great friends with a man called Mahesha. They talked every day and got to know everything about each other. They became like brothers and swore to visit holy places together, if ever they got out of prison. Mahesha was named for *Shiva* because in Sanskrit Mahesha means Supreme Lord, which of course is Lord *Shiva*. He said it was his life's aim to visit Shiva's temple in Ghinghu in the Himalayas. Morardada agreed to accompany him and in return Mahesha would visit Shirdi.

'But the hard labour killed him, so Morardada said we would go together to pray for Mahesha and his family. Then he too died before we could make the journey; but now I will do what he could not. So when you pray remember Mahesha, for Morardada.'

My family always imparts information slowly and sparsely so there is an element of jeopardy or irritation in everything we do. I had travelled well over a thousand miles under the impression that we were planning to enjoy the scenery and visit historic hilltop towns. Instead I was on a real *jatra*. We had suffered the uncomfortable journey so that we could be closer to the gods and were facing more torment and the purging of our souls. Snow-capped peaks loomed menacingly over the town of Ghinghu as the train pulled in. I shivered and pulled a jumper and a scarf from my bag. The locals were dressed lightly, as if it were high summer, and tourists could be distinguished by their heavy layers of clothing. I felt like a soft southerner arriving in Newcastle on a cold day, being greeted by bare-chested Geordies.

Our hotel, which was called The Comfort, had a worrying leaning façade lined with cracks and the grime of decades. It was a notch lower in class than The Suprim and the food was worse. Gujarati cuisine is considered the spiciest and most varied in all India and Himalayan food does not have the same cachet. We were served a prison diet of gloopy rice and bland *dhal*, half the plate filled with tasteless dumplings, a delicacy copied from the Chinese to fill hungry stomachs in a colder climate. My room was cool but I was afraid to use the blankets because they had disturbing multi-coloured stains and a beetle scuttled out of one of the folds. It was too chilly for lizards and the absence of cockroaches did not bode well for the hygiene of my room. A visit to the dirty bathroom confirmed *Bapuji's* theory that they prefer hygienic lodgings. *'Ram, Ram. Ram...'*

The vista was wonderful, but I had not come to India to experience the cold. We had that in Leicester. The temperature had dropped by twenty-five degrees Celsius and we took a rickshaw to the temple site stuffed inside thick layers of clothes. En route Bhulima barked out an order to the driver to stop at a shop and emerged clutching brown paper bags containing dozens of bananas.

'Once you are in the Himalayas proper you have to be very careful. The food is dirty, unfit for Gujaratis from the south. If we ate it we would be sick for days. I have heard of people getting dysentery and being in hospital for months after just one meal. The water is lovely and clean, but you can't survive on that, so until we get back to the hotel we eat only bananas, the only safe food we can carry.' She threw me two bunches and divided up the rest. A friend of mine had returned from India with dysentery and had only just survived after losing half his body weight. We had sent a get-well card on which someone had written 'Don't start any long books.' He had a good sense of humour, but didn't find it funny. Remembering him on his drip, fighting for his life, I decided to follow Bhulima's advice and stuffed the bananas into my duffel bag. Paying homage to the gods was tougher than I imagined.

One banana later we arrived at the *mandir* complex, where a gift shop was selling the usual gaudy *Shiva* merchandise. Next to it was a new brick building with a large chalkboard outside and scrawled on this was some barely legible Hindi writing and an English translation: '*Toolet. Best modin lukshery Europin toolet 5 rupees, Indian toolet 1 rupee. Pleeze kip clin.*' The rickshaw dropped up off just beyond the toolet by a fast-flowing river gurgling over stones and rocks and forming a series of waterfalls. My eyes were drawn to the small but perfectly formed shrine nestled high above us, surrounded by slanting birch trees. The main building had orange, blue, yellow and green columns supporting a marble dome with a fluttering red flag. Dwarfing it in height but not width was a glinting golden *lingham*, the mark of *Shiva*. I looked at *Ba* and Bhulima to see whether the giant erect phallus, symbol of creation and fertility, caused them any embarrassment. It did not. Their faces were overcome by reverence and their lips again moved rapidly in inaudible prayer.

I looked back at the *mandir* and it was only now that I noticed the stunning setting. Behind it the river forked and both sides gushed down before reuniting in front of the facade. Halfway down, perched on a stone, was a small blue-grey statue of *Shiva*. He was sitting cross-legged, two of his four arms folded low in prayer, the other two raising a *tamru* and trident. A large notice warned pilgrims that the climb was unsuitable for the infirm, involving a steep ascent on a dirt track followed by exactly a thousand steps. *Ba* and *Bapuji* were sprightly, but I doubted whether Bhulima could manage either climb. I jokingly offered to carry her up but she said that would not be necessary and pointed to the end of the road where half a dozen elephants were waiting for customers. We chose one and the *mahout* ordered it to sit down while we climbed onto the *howdah*, then we lumbered up the precipitous path, swaying gently as the elephant shifted its weight from one side to the other. I sat at the front next to the *mahout*.

'Where are you from?'

'London, England.' I had long ago stopped saying I was from Leicester as no one had heard of it.

'London is big, big money capital. Many rich people there. Do you have stocks and shares, *sahib*?'

'No.'

'That is good because they can go up and they can go down. Most unreliable. But there is one investment guaranteed to make money. Have you thought of buying an elephant?

'No.'

'Consider this, *sahib*. You buy a baby elephant and I train it, then the elephant works for at least sixty years. Even after you pay for feed you are making money because I will be using it to move timber in the forest. More money than any stock market, guaranteed. Would you like to buy an elephant? Or, perhaps, many elephants? I can arrange. Very good price.'

I told him I'd think about it and he gave me his details. As we arrived at the plateau which marked the start of the giant stairway I asked him how the elephant would manage the narrowest sections. He laughed and pointed at my feet: from now on we would have to walk. Large rectangles, big enough for a family car, had been drawn into the dirt and he guided the elephant into its designated parking space. No car would ever climb this road.

Bhulima alighted and marched off towards a group of scruffy-looking men drinking *Thums Up* and smoking *bidis* under a neem tree and haggled with them until they settled on a price. She then plonked herself onto a large rectangular stool covered in sackcloth for comfort which, once hoisted up by ropes tied to a bamboo stick, became a portable makeshift swing. Two of our cut-price sherpas walked in front, two at the back, their shoulders padded with folded towels.

'*Achha, chalo, chalo.*' Bhulima pointed at the shine and we were on our way.

She was oblivious to the comic figure she cut, her plump legs dangling wildly out of control and her open-toed *champals* in constant danger of flying away. When the ascent began she swung from side to side as the steps were bumpy, uneven and varied in height. A fifth sherpa led the way, occasionally chivvying people out of the way on the narrow stone-stairway to *Shiva*. His co-workers were strong and they needed to be because Bhulima weighed more than eleven stone and by the two hundredth step they were starting to wilt. They took a breather whenever we reached a wide-enough platform and we were grateful, as we needed one too. The mountain air was not refreshing and invigorating, as promoted by the movies. It was very thin and it was easy to get out of breath. After almost an hour, wheezing and gasping, we arrived at the *mandir* after. Throughout the ages pilgrims have suffered to approach the gods and today we had earned all the blessings *Shiva* could bestow. The climb had made us all hungry, so we delved into our banana bags.

The scale of the climb meant there were no crowds. Only around thirty pilgrims were inside the shrine and the mantra *'Om namah Shivaya'* echoed around the chamber. It was a familiar refrain which I remembered from funerals and the atmosphere here was equally sombre. A *Brahmin* in orange robes, dwarfed by a giant effigy of *Shiva*, was conducting blessings in front of his rapt congregation: everyone but me seemed to believe they were somehow in the presence of *Shiva* himself. The pilgrims' expressions suggested that they could sense and touch him and that by coming here they could appeal to him directly. I remembered that I had to pray for Mahesha and did so. Really I wanted to go outside to take pictures of the views, but out of a sense of guilt I lingered at the shrine. The worshippers had an intensity of belief I envied. I was not an atheist or an agnostic. Throughout my school years I had attended Christian assemblies. I had Muslim and Sikh friends and we often argued about our religions, but my faith was compromised and lacking in clarity. Yet in times of trouble I had only one recourse: *'Ram, Ram, Ram...'*

The *puja* lasted almost an hour and we were then ushered into an adjoining room. In the middle, in front of another Shiva statue, an oil lamp was fiercely burning, creating dark dancing shadows all around. In one corner sat a cross-legged hairless *Brahmin,* his face barely visible in the gloom.

*'Namaste.* You are in the presence of the *'Anant Lau'*, the divine eternal light which has been burning here for hundreds of years. If the flame is ever extinguished then disaster will fall upon the world, so it is incumbent on us to keep it alive. Please, take time to pray so Shiva may grant your wishes, and give alms to the poor.'

More fervent prayers were offered and *Bapuji* emptied his pockets of rupees. We exited by a side door to find the sherpas dozing in a circle around the trunk of a giant oak tree. They quickly got to their feet and braced themselves for the Hanumanean task ahead as Bhulima placed her considerable bulk onto the seat and they heaved her onto their shoulders. She began munching her bananas and we did the same. Our stomachs were crying out for *samosas* and *bhel*, but bananas were all we had.

I joined the leader and offered him one, which he refused, then asked about his family. He had eight children but two had died soon after they were born. Four were girls, so they would cost him a fortune in dowries when they married, and he was pinning his hopes on the two boys to look after him when he became old. When did he plan to retire? He said that once he reached forty-five or fifty he might be ready to stop. His aim was to provide the boys with a good education, which was why he worked seven days a week. He would have liked to educate the girls too, but it was expensive. I thought of his sons reaping the benefits of an education at the expense of their sisters and forgot the spectacular scenery around me. The same thing had happened in our family. Money had been put aside for *Bapuji* and his younger brother to attend college in Munsari, but not for their sister, Laxmi. *Ba*, who was very intelligent, had also missed out on an education. I had been sent to England at an early age specifically to attend a good school, but my sister Kumud had been left behind. Choices had been made and the result was gross unfairness; though it was a while since I had even thought of it. I needed something to shake me out of my reverie and perhaps *Shiva* was watching over me, because a familiar belch followed by guttural spitting had the desired effect. I saw that red kites with their trademark long forked tails were swirling around us, their wings angled but hardly moving as they glided on the currents, and the sheer splendour of their flight against that backdrop lifted my gloomy daydream.

At the bottom the rickshaw was waiting and as we rounded a sharp bend we met a cluster of langur monkeys lazing by the roadside. I made the driver pull over, got out and began to take photographs. I remembered that I still had three bananas left and threw them towards the langurs, causing an outburst of chattering and fighting. *Bapuji* climbed out with the remaining bananas and helped quell the riot. *Shiva* had ensured that not only were we feeding the poor; we were caring for his monkey subjects.

The *jatra* had come to an end and after two punitive days on the train we returned to Ganeshgam, physically drained and spiritually replenished. Kohli and Amisha were standing outside the house looking utterly terrified.

'Snake, snake, big snake has gone in,' cried Amisha. Her enormous brown eyes were open wide and swivelling around like Kaa's in *The Jungle Book*. 'Jitenda is in there with Horidada looking for it but it's hiding somewhere.'

A crash and a few wallops reverberated through the open door and a few moments afterwards Jitenda emerged exultant, holding the flattened snake in both hands. He was followed by an ecstatic Horidada clutching a cudgel. It had been a most handsome creature, its brown body artistically flecked with random yellow and green patterns, but now its head resembled that of a boxer who had taken a good beating.

'This is a bad omen, a very bad omen. I prayed and prayed to *Shiva* to keep our house safe and free from snakes while we were away,' Bhulima confided to me. 'He does not always grant our wishes and when evil befalls us we must treat it as a warning. We must behave better and treat others with kindness, or worse will follow.'

What followed was an endless round of long and boring visits to relatives and friends and friends of relatives. Ummi flew back to England the following day, Raj was away sorting out his visa and Sunil busy on his farm, so there was no one my age around to keep me company. Finally, after a long week, the arrival of our taxi with its freshly garlanded *Rama* marked the completion of my return to India. We were stacking our luggage in the boot when I glimpsed a sharp-faced grey and brown creature scampering to the front of the house. It scurried straight to Bhulima, who was sitting patiently on the *charpoy* on the verandah, waiting to say goodbye. It sat up in front of her and begged, its front paws outstretched like a meerkat's and emitted a series of high-pitched chirps. With tears streaming down her face, Bhulima looked up at the heavens and raised her hands in prayer.

It was a mongoose, returning after a long absence, for Bhulima's rice and *chappatis*.

# SECOND COURSE

*I have extremely hazy memories of being five years old.*
*I can, however, recollect some impressions: odd and different smells*
*and strange vibrant colours. At that age I experienced a number of*
*unforgettable incidents, such as sighting exotic animals I had never*
*imagined and a catastrophic journey across the plains of Africa.*
*By speaking to those who were there*
*I have been able to paint a clearer picture.*

*To those horrified by the occasional bigoted remarks*
*recorded here I can only say that they originated in a different era,*
*in villages where prejudices were passed on.*
*Those who cringe now may have themselves reacted similarly then.*
*This is a tale of its time.*

# Chapter 11

## The unexpected funeral

If the journey from Mumbai to Ganeshgam was dangerous, then the one to Zambia in Africa was disastrous. The three thousand mile expedition by taxi, ship and van was expected to take around ten days. It took almost twice as long and encompassed a serious injury for me, a near-death experience for *Ba*, a fatality and a funeral.

*Bapuji* had wired *Ba* the many rupees we needed to buy our passage out of India. When we set off I had no idea where we were going, only that it would involve a reunion with my father after a long absence. My mud-eating sister Kumud was three and I, the spoilt would-be little prince who yearned for new clothes every day, was five, almost six. We were accompanied by *Nana, Bapuji's* younger brother, a reassuring presence for *Ba* on such an expedition.

The dimensions of the ship were eye-popping. Judging by the size of the baying multitude battling to board, it was as if the whole of Ganeshgam was about to be packed inside a giant floating object. I had once sunk a flat piece of wood in the village lake by loading it with stones, so logic indicated the ship would similarly go under. *Nana* assured me it would not, but could not explain why.

I calculated that from our house our destination was fifteen times more distant than Mumbai and one hundred times more than Surat. The rigorous Indian maths teaching helped me realise this journey would take a long time. Kumud, however, was constantly wondering if we would see *Bapuji* that day. When told no, she would ask the same question an hour later and start to whine. The mud she'd eaten may have been affecting her brain.

I remember little about the voyage apart from sleeping in lumpy bunks in the badly-lit hot bowels of the ship and playing endless games with other travelling children, who had quickly become my best mates. *Ba* had become friends with a lone traveller the same age as herself and with the same name as her sister, Kusummasi. She was from Munsari and was also going to join her husband who, like *Bapuji*, had ventured into deepest Africa. They chattered and giggled nonstop, keeping a watchful eye on our raucous antics and sipping *masala* tea. Occasionally *Nana* would replace them as guardian and we were careful not to be as noisy when he was in charge.

Every day we ran amok on the decks, chasing each other or playing hide and seek. Looking back it seems a crazy idea, but sailing third-class across the Indian Ocean was much cheaper than flying. We were about to discover that it was also more hazardous.

On the third day a severe storm rocked the ship. The waves were so large they smashed violently on the sides and rose up, soaking any passengers near the rails. *Ba* ushered us down three flights of steps, which seemed to be swaying madly under our feet, and back along the corridor to the cabin. We were confined to our dark abode and warned to sit on our bunk beds and keep still until the gale subsided. I wanted to go out and play, but she said the wind was so strong it would carry me up and whisk me away to a place where only *sadhus* lived, deep under the water, and we'd never be together again.

'Do you want to disappear and never see us again and live with the *sadhus*?'

'No'.

'Well, keep still and stay where you are until I tell you, or the *sadhus* will come for you.'

I awoke the following day to find a strange man in a long white coat leaning over me. He peered down at me through the largest spectacles I had ever seen. My head was throbbing with pain and covered in bandages. I cried out for *Ba* and she and *Nana* appeared reassuringly quickly from behind the stranger. I could see Kusummasi sitting in the corner holding my sleeping sister.

They told me that after the storm abated I had been running full tilt down a metal staircase, had come crashing down and lost consciousness. My forehead had been split open and the man who was standing by the side of the bed had stitched it together again. *Ba* explained that he was a doctor, like the one who had removed my tonsils. I had broken no bones but had dark swellings on my arms, legs and bottom. I had no memory of my accident.

'If he'd been bigger and heavier he'd have suffered many more injuries, but he's fine,' the man reassured *Ba*. 'At his age children bounce like a ball. Give him two of these tablets three times a day.'

He handed over a brown bottle and examined me with his stethoscope. He then pushed a thermometer into my mouth, checked it, smiled and abruptly left. I was still groggy but surprisingly hungry and demanded a full *thali*, *samosas* and *jalebis*, which *Nana* was sent to fetch. The following day I was back running around the deck but forbidden from climbing the stairs without supervision.

On the eighth day we reached Dar es Salaam in Tanzania and I took my first step on another continent. I knew India was full of people who were unlike us Patels: *sadhus*, snake charmers, *Dalits*, Sikhs with their turbans, Muslims men with their beards and *kufis* and Muslim women in their *hijabs*; but they were all Indian and oddly familiar. Africans were even more exotic. I was fascinated by the shape and colour of their faces, their curly hair and the gleaming whiteness of their teeth. They seemed to be bigger, stronger and lither than we were.

The smells were very different, lacking in spice but initially enticing, especially the aroma wafting from the ubiquitous red roast corn hand carts. This soon merged unpleasantly with one of the most repulsive stenches I'd ever come across.

'What is that horrible stink? It's going to make me sick.'

'Fish!' *Ba* too had turned up her nose in disgust. 'They eat fish here. Lots of it and they cook it on a fire and that is what you can smell. *Bapuji* wrote to me about it. They eat the bones too sometimes, if the fish are not too big. Can you imagine that? We are pure vegetarian but even in India there are people who eat fish, like the *Kori* Patels. But I'm sure even they don't eat the bones.'

'Who are the *Kori* Patels?'

'They are Patels who live by the sea and eat fish almost every day. Which is why they always smell of it.'

'I'm glad we're not *Kori* Patels. I could never eat fish: they are so disgusting and slimy. Why would you eat fish when you can eat *kachoris* and *pendas*?'

Our luggage was loaded on to a cart and trundled to the car park by porters oblivious of my constant staring. I was struggling to understand that not everybody in the world was brown. In books I'd seen strange creatures with a dozen heads and demons who breathed fire, but not once had I seen anyone who was black. The people now surrounding us were beyond my imagination.

Kumud and I were both expecting to be met by *Bapuji* but we were deeply disappointed. *Ba* explained that *Bapuji* was very busy so he had sent two of his friends to pick us up in a large van. This led to another bout of crying from Kumud, quietened only by the appearance of boiled sweets, of which I too was a beneficiary.

Jayantikaka and Jagdishkaka were brothers and both had twirling moustaches and thick wavy hair. Their curls were different from African ones and I spent the next few minutes trying to work out what made them dissimilar. I concluded that the locals had tighter locks and Indians had longer, more unruly hair, but that was the limit of my deductions.

*Ba* had invited Kusummasi to travel with us as she too was on her way to Nkuzu in Zambia. Of all the decisions she made in her life, this was the one *Ba* would most regret. Kusummasi was planning to go by train, but decided it would be better to travel in company. It would take us at least three days to reach our new home.

The two drivers worked in shifts to cover the eleven hundred miles to

Nkuzu and we did not even stop at night because we slept in the car. There was a lot of red dust swirling around us as we jolted and jounced across the plains, often on unmade roads, heading south west from Dar es Salaam. Just after dawn on the second day we took a long break at a hotel which was run by a family of Patels from Munsari and all had a bath. It is a mortal sin for a Hindu to walk around for long unwashed.

We slept a lot. Kumud and I were nuisances: full of demands which could not be met, moaning constantly. There was little to keep us amused and we soon tired of the unremarkable scenery. Initially I found the local people interesting, but while they were different, their mode of living was familiar to me: the women effortlessly carried copper vessels on their heads; the men were burdened by impossibly large loads on their backs; people worked in the fields and goats and cattle were tethered by mud huts in the villages. The men were often bare-chested, wearing only short ragged lengths of cloth around their loins. The women did not wear *saris*. Instead they were dressed in colourful two-piece outfits with vivid randomly-shaped patterns I had never seen before. I was disappointed because the roads were not filled with cows, boars and camels. Africa was staid compared to the hustle bustle of India.

On the second day, not long after darkness had fallen, I was awoken by a sudden screeching of brakes. The car jerked forward and came to a sudden violent halt. Kumud and I, asleep on the back seat, were hurled off it. The door to our left was wide open and a warm wind was blowing in. The men at the front jumped out shouting, screaming, panic-stricken; barking orders at each other. 'You look over there, I'll look down here.'

The headlights were on, illuminating the gloom. Torches moved all around us, lighting up bushes and rocks then leaving them invisible again as the bearer moved away. I looked for *Ba* but could not see her anywhere, so I bawled as loudly as I could and Kumud did the same as we clung to each other.

Several years later *Ba* and *Nana* told me what had happened. We had left the flatlands and begun a gentle ascent through some fertile hills dotted with sizeable settlements. The three men at the front were wide awake, while on the back seat all four of us were sound asleep, Kumud and I lying curled up together. *Ba* was next to us and she was leaning heavily on Kusummasi, who in turn was wedged against the door, using it as a pillow. The door had not been properly shut after our last stop and as we rounded a bend at more than forty miles an hour it had sprung open and they both tumbled out.

*Nana* hauled Kumud and me out of the van and held us close, vainly trying to stop our shrieking. Jayantikaka and Jagdishkaka had both disappeared, searching for their two missing passengers. They tracked back and found *Ba,* lying by the roadside, a few inches from a precipice. She was still conscious but covered in cuts and grazes. A little further back they saw a body lying in a pool of blood amid the rocks on a ledge about ten yards down.

I remember the panic, mayhem, lights flashing and time expanding. Kumud and I had little idea of the gravity of the situation but we knew instinctively that something terrible had happened. Nana reassured us that everything was fine, but we knew it was not.

'Where is *Ba*? I want *Ba.*'

'She is hurt, like you were on the ship, but it's nothing to worry about. Jagdishkaka is with her and she'll be fine. Jayantikaka is going to fetch a doctor. She'll be back with you very soon, I promise you.'

A mile or so ahead of us were the bright lights of a city and Jayantikaka drove away to get help. By the time he returned Kumud and I had both gone back to sleep in *Nana's* arms, exhausted by our own crying.

Patels are rarely alone in the world. They have colonised more of the globe than Alexander the Great, Genghis Khan and Adolf Hitler. You will find them in the Hebrides, Australia, Hong Kong and Canada. Even close to the beginning of their world conquest, even in a location as remote as this, Jayantikaka found kith and kin from his birthplace, Rajkot in the Gujarat. They had set up a textile factory in Mwunza, the city not far from the scene of our accident, where they owned a large and spacious home which became our haven. *Ba*, Kumud and I were told, was in hospital but would be coming back later that day. In the meantime a succession of newly acquired *kakas, kakis, mamas, masis, dadas* and *mas* fussed around us. Even those not remotely related acquire a family title as a mark of respect. After the shock we had suffered they gave in to our every wish or greedy demand.

That afternoon a heavily-bandaged *Ba* arrived by rickshaw and we had a tearful reunion. She held us close in the folds of her sari, which was still dirty, dust-stained and slightly torn. She said *Rama* had saved her. He was looking after her and he would look after us, if we continued to behave well. I asked her where Kusummasi was and she told us she was now with *Shiva* in a place far, far away and would return one day. I began asking awkward questions about how she had reached Shiva and when we would see her, but *Ba* would not elaborate. She took us to the *kulfi* vendor, who had parked his cart nearby.

Over the next twenty-four hours there was much whispering among the adults. We lived through the rituals of a funeral without grasping what we were experiencing. People in Ganeshgam had died and I had picked up details of what that entailed by osmosis, but the subject remained largely a mystery. Telegrams were sent to Kusummasi's husband in Zambia and her relatives in India, to tell them what had happened. They would be unable to get to the funeral and because of the demands of tradition the decision was taken to cremate the body as soon as possible.

Our funerals are never a minor event. Even though she had no friends or relatives in Tanzania, Kusummasi's death was marked by a succession of mourners, all of them immigrants from the Gujarat who had settled here. They arrived and sat around for hours, paying their respects and looking solemn. To stop us becoming infected by this melancholy Kumud and I were kept in the garden, where there was a swing hung from a tree and a plastic ball to keep us amused.

We were shielded from the final funeral rites, when the body was brought to the house and given its final blessing by a *Brahmin.* Chanting mourners circled the casket, throwing rice and flowers inside. Those closest to Kusummasi, the four adults in our van, anointed her with a *tilak* to speed up her safe passage out of the world. We were introduced to children of a similar age whose parents had arrived for the funeral and their mother stayed in the garden and played hide and seek with us. She was not very good at it and always left a foot or elbow sticking out. Her children knew the best places to disappear as the garden was familiar to them and were annoyingly difficult to find.

There was no way of avoiding the cremation itself as everyone has to attend. *Ba* held Kumud in her arms and I clung to her sari and watched wide-eyed as the casket arrived in a cart pulled by a pair of grey oxen. Kusummasi was placed on top of a funeral pyre made of wood and straw. It was dramatically set alight by a man carrying a burning torch. The blue and yellow flames instantly rose high and acrid smoke billowed upwards and away. The heat was intense and there were crackling and hissing noises reminiscent of fireworks. I was mesmerised and intrigued by the process. Kusummasi's body had turned to ashes, but I knew she would not feel any pain. Her soul was indestructible but had to be released and it would return in another form. At least a hundred mourners had come to the funeral of someone whom, apart from the six of us, nobody knew.

*Bapuji* once told me that good behaviour is vital throughout your life because it ensures that you will return as a higher being, richer and wiser. Bad behaviour will result in transformation into something less desirable; perhaps even a rat, or a snake. This was a terrifying thought guaranteed to transform us into angels, some of the time. Whenever I saw a rodent I wondered how terrible that person had been in his previous life and prayed that if I did err, I would at least return as an elephant or a mongoose. I hoped Kusummasi would come back as a *maharani*. She had been really nice.

A policeman approached *Ba* and handed her an envelope. As they had no lingua franca he communicated in sign language, pointing vehemently at the pyre and making a circle around his neck with his hands. *Ba* looked baffled, so he jabbed a finger at the envelope and she opened it. Inside was a gold necklace belonging to Kusummasi. *Ba* smiled and thanked him by cupping her hands in prayer and bowing her head towards him. The envelope disappeared deep into her sari, which had no pockets.

We returned to the house and everybody had to bathe, as death leaves you impure, and afterwards the servants began cleansing the rooms. Only after this is anyone allowed to eat. The process is completed on the twelfth day, when a *Brahmin* conducts *puja* and blesses the house by lighting *agarbattis*. On the sixth day Kusummasi's husband, Bhikhumama, arrived from Nkuzu.

He wanted to hear all the details, so Kumud and I were again whisked away to play outside. When we were allowed to return we saw *Ba* rummage in the folds of her sari and produce the crumpled envelope. Bhikhumama opened it and gave it back to her.

'You keep the necklace, Dhaniben. I have no need for it. Kusum would want you to have it.'

It was time for us to set off for Nkuzu. The journey was uneventful, if uncomfortable. We dozed like dogs all our way to Zambia, occasionally baying for food and drink. Once we were silenced in mid-howl when we came across a pair of the tallest animals we had ever seen. Their legs alone were much taller than *Nana*. They had astonishingly long necks and what appeared to be two enormous thumbs jutting out of the top of their heads, between their ears. They were greedily pulling leaves off the very top of a tree as we sped past.

*'E su che?'*

'What is that?'

*Ba* shrugged her shoulders.

*'Khaburr ni.'*

'I don't know.'

She poked *Nana,* in the front seat, but he had never seen one before He turned to Jagdishkaka.

*'E jiruf che. Eni pase hathi ho bo nandhlo dekhai.'*

'It's a jiruf. Even an elephant looks small next to it.'

We had arrived in a land of giant creatures. For the first time I felt a sense of excitement about my new home.

# Chapter 12

## The black sadhus

We drove into Nzuka past huge whitewashed houses covered in red and white bougainvillea, with landscaped gardens and fruit orchards. Sprinklers moved lazily over the neat lawns with what appeared to be mini rainbows dancing across the tops of the highest drops. Under the spray African women wearing bright yellow headscarves were manicuring the lawns with scissors. Arcing around elaborate fountains were marble statues of naked men and women on plinths, the men showing off and the women staring ahead, bored. One attracted my attention: a happy little boy relieving himself, the water emerging in a constant stream and splashing down further away than seemed humanly possible.

'This is where the *gorias* live,' said Jagdishkaka. 'They are very nice people, mostly from England, who eat meat and fish all day, every day. We live on the other side of the river.'

'What are *gorias*? Where is England?'

'It is a country far, far away, very different to ours and the *gorias* are the people who live there. They have white skin, not brown like us, and they don't like the heat or the sun. That is why you almost never see them: they are always indoors. They do not like the outside much, so they stay inside in England all day too. That is because it is almost always too cold there, like the Himalayas, and very often covered in snow. If it is not snowing, it is raining. They have a horrible climate! I will show you some pictures.'

'Is their country full of big mountains like the Himalayas?'

So it went until we crossed a bridge with a large group of bungalows to the right and a forest to the left. A dry ditch ran along both sides of the road, forming a clear boundary. Booming through the trees we could hear drums: a different sound and rhythm to the *tablas* we knew. These were loud and frightening, yet there was an excitement throbbing from them which *tablas* could not match.

We turned sharply over a makeshift wooden bridge towards the houses and there, waiting for us, was a familiar figure. We squealed with delight. It was *Bapuji;* but he looked different. His *dhoti* had been replaced by a white shirt and brown trousers and he had something red with blue stripes tied neatly around his neck with a strange knot. He was sporting sunglasses, which made him sinister. Kumud burst into tears and I was puzzled. Why was *Bapuji* dressed like the men in the *Journey to the Centre of the Earth* film? When he whipped off the sunglasses *Bapuji* was almost back, but not quite. As he drew us into his arms, bowing to hold us closer, we received a blast of something pungent, a cross between fading flowers and herbs and spices, neither pleasant nor unpleasant. Kumud sniffed the air like a wild dog and her lower lip made a fully-formed *jibroo*. *Bapuji* burst out laughing.

'It's my aftershave you can smell. You will get used to it.'

'What is aftershave?'

'After I shave every morning I put it on my face because shaving can be quite painful and you sometimes cut yourself. It's like a cream you use when you are hurt and it smells nice. All the men here buy it. It's called Old Spice.' We were not convinced, but *Ba* seemed to like it.

*Bapuji* wanted to know whether we liked Africa and we told him about the jiruf.

'It was taller than four men!' As she spoke Kumud's *jibroo* unfurled. 'Higher than any house in Ganeshgam.'

*Bapuji* said the jirufs were the tallest animals in the whole world and they could only be found in Africa. There were also elephants even bigger than those in India and he promised to show us a herd. He asked about *Bhulima* and we entered the house, where we were greeted by the owners, Naginkaka and Hemakaki. *Bapuji* had been living with them since his arrival. Two black servants, both men, brought in bottles with foreign labels containing an ice-cold orange drink and two small bags which also bore undecipherable symbols. Naginkaka opened them and rummaged around inside until he found a small sachet in each one. He tore them both open and sprinkled the contents into the bags.

'What's inside?'

'The English call them 'potato kips'. They're made with *bataka*. Try them, you'll like them. That white stuff is just *mithu*.'

'What's this drink?'

'Fanta. It tastes like oranges. You see, it's written here in English. You will be learning this language soon.'

The Fanta was immediately seductive. If at first we were unsure about the bland taste of the flat golden kips we quickly found them addictive, especially when washed down with the fizzing orange nectar. This was our introduction to exotic foreign food. Munching and slurping happily, my eyes were drawn to the label on the bottle. Written Gujarati has no vowels, so their sounds are added by placing tiny symbols around the consonants. 'Fanta', therefore, should have three letters, f, n and t, plus two symbols. Why was this word written with five letters? It was incomprehensible. English would be very difficult to learn. Probably impossible.

It was getting dark and the adults wanted to discuss the events of the last few days, so we were taken to bed and *Ba* recounted heroic deeds from the *Ramayana* until we fell asleep. I awoke after a dreamless night and was able to admire our new toilet in full daylight. It was an upmarket hole in the ground with ceramic tiles in sky blue set around it. As a bonus the building adjoined the back of the house, so there was no need to brave a monkey troop before relieving yourself. There was also a green canopy so you wouldn't get wet, even in the monsoon season. The bath house was next door, better constructed and decorated than ours, but the inside was familiar: a rickety tap which hissed and gurgled, a navy blue plastic bucket and an uneven jug which tumbled over when placed on its base, to my delight.

Breakfast was disappointing as there were no kips or Fanta and we had to make do with *chevro* and *puris* with milk. This was brought in by the two servants, who were introduced to us as Chikondi and Mwala. They both had permanent smiles and seemed very nice. Hemakaki would shout 'Boy' whenever she wanted them and *Ba,* after several attempts at pronouncing their names, decided the feat was impossible. Kumud and I managed to say them, but Ba opted for a simpler solution: she called the older servant 'Boy One' and the younger, 'Boy Two'.

The naming ceremony over, *Bapuji* put on his strange uniform and splashed himself with Old Spice. He said he would be back later and dashed away. We watched him mount a scooter and he vanished in a puff of smoke, leaving a trail of diesel behind. *Ba* saw the look of disappointment on our faces and assured us he would buy us *kulfi* later.

'Where has *Bapuji* gone? To our farm?'

'No, we don't have a farm here. He's gone to work.'

*Ba* explained to us that *Bapuji* was an accountant. He worked for a very big shop in Nzuka where he did all the sums. He worked out how many items like shoes and clothes had been sold each day, how much money had been paid for them and how many products needed replacing. I thought it sounded dull compared to his life in India.

'In Ganeshgam he didn't have to work for anybody and he could play with us whenever he wanted and we had our own big house. Why have we come here?'

'You'll like it here. You will see.' *Ba* did not sound convinced.

*Bapuji* returned late that afternoon and Jagdishkaka took us all out in his van. As we drove through the centre of Nzuka *Bapuji* pointed out places of interest, like Robinson Brothers, the shop where he worked, and the *mandir*. We stopped briefly at a cart to buy *kulfis* and I was allowed to pay for them in *kwachas*, the local currency. The streets were thronging with Africans, but the English were nowhere to be seen. It was, as Jagdishkaka had said, too hot for them. But just as we came round a corner two sombre-looking Englishmen emerged from a shop. I stared at them, puzzled and deeply disappointed. They didn't have white skin at all. Their faces were very red.

Over the next few days we met our neighbours and explored our enclave. It was not far from the centre of Nzuka and comprised clusters of bungalows of varying sizes inhabited by several hundred people from the Surat area. Three thousand miles from our native land we had somehow found each other and gathered here like pack animals for comfort and company. We had set up shops where we could buy most of the familiar things we desired: food, clothes, furniture, even *tablas*. It was home from home; but I was missing my friends.

*Ba's* first attempt to pair me up with a boy my age ended in failure. Sailesh was the cleverest boy in the enclave, but also the most obnoxious. Sharp-eyed and sharp-nosed, he reminded me of a red kite, the ultimate foe of my favourite animal, the mongoose. He loved to pinch me or push me over whenever no one was looking and my retaliation was always spotted. I was chastised for my unsociable behaviour.

I had already worked out that there were no *sadhus* in Nzuka, which made it difficult for *Ba* to deal with my bad conduct. In Ganeshgam we had no boundaries, but here *Ba* was more wary and became angry if I disappeared for long, playing and exploring. She scolded me when she caught me about to enter the forest, telling me it was a very dangerous place. It was full of enormous fierce animals and as they liked eating little boys I should steer clear. I made a mental note to go there as soon as I could.

*Ba* decided a spot of prayer might calm me down so she dragged me to the *mandir* and we both prayed for my redemption, she fervently, I less so. She was concerned that demons had taken over my body; I was resentful as I had done little wrong. '*Ram, Ram, Ram*,' I prayed. 'Show the world that Sailesh is a nasty boy and needs to be punished.'

Alongside the *mandir* was a small school which would be my seat of learning for the next three years. Chikondi was given the task of escorting me there and back each day and I could not have had a kinder chaperone. His face was constantly lit with the sheer joy of life. Whenever he heard music or drums he would start to dance. His limbs became liquid and he was suddenly lost in another world, oblivious to his surroundings. I wondered whether eating meat and fish as he did made people jollier. My family was contented enough, but hardly radiated happiness from every pore like Chikondi.

Until my first day at school I had no idea where he and Mwala lived. They always seemed to be around, magically appearing whenever they were called. One day *Bapuji* took me to the garage at the bottom of the garden and shouted their names. Chikondi came out, brushing his tightly-knotted hair with a large brown and yellow comb. Through the open door and I could see two makeshift beds on the floor. This was their home.

Chikondi and I communicated in sign language, which was initially difficult but soon became easier. He then began teaching me some basics of the local dialect, which was a mixture of his tribal language and Swahili. He would point out objects and tell me what they were in his language and I would do likewise. After all these years odd words stick. 'Mmwenye' was the first one I learned as it means 'Indian'. 'Ndilekeni' translates as 'leave me alone' and 'vena aikone mooisay' as 'I don't like you', two phrases I was keen to learn so that I could spit them at Sailesh.

Chikondi was obsessed with motors, so I became familiar with words like 'gari' (car), which, oddly enough, was almost the same in Gujarati. I was stunned by this revelation, but we didn't share enough words to discuss it. He was good at introducing new words, especially those reflecting his passion. Once he indicated a roundabout and said, 'Kiplefti'. I mastered the word and delighted in its sound. It was more than a decade later that I realised it was a bastardisation of the English.

The school was more modern than the one in Ganeshgam. Although there was no apartheid in Zambia only Indians, more specifically Gujaratis, attended. Almost all of us lived cheek by jowl on the same estate and the daily register was entirely familiar: Anookbhai, Bharatkumar, Chandulal, Dilipkumar and so on. One difference was that we had desks and adjusting to sitting on a chair instead of on the ground was difficult. I felt an uncontrollable urge to fidget. I would tap my fingers, move my toes around or lift and lower the front of my feet, activities that were trickier on the floor. Our teacher was Shastriji, a portly man with a pot belly. He had a massive head to go with his huge ears, burly hands and permanently flared nostrils. He reminded me of Ganesh without the trunk but I knew it was wrong to compare a human being to a god. *'Ram, Ram, Ram...'*

Shastriji had a rough grating voice and snorted like a wounded wild boar between sentences, which made each one sound like an important announcement. He had a voice to wake the dead, not just loud but booming, rasping, reverberating and commanding. It reminded me of the fury of the gods in a Bollywood movie, when a disembodied voice would come down from the heavens and everyone watching seemed frozen in time, terrified. I decided to be on my best behaviour.

We began the day with maths. Shastriji was writing on the blackboard to explain simple multiplication when Sailesh, at the desk behind me, pinched me hard on my neck. Instinctively I turned and hit him, equally hard. I believed in justice. He screamed and Shastriji swivelled round, glared and beckoned us both to the front of the class. He placed me at his left, Sailesh at his right and pinched my sore earlobe between finger and huge thumb until I too screamed. Sailesh came in for harsher treatment as he took longer to squeal, having a higher pain threshold. Shastriji's applied increasing pressure on his earlobe and eventually there was a yelp. The pressure continued and the ear turned redder and redder until Sailesh began howling. Seeing my arch enemy in severe pain was discomforting, even for me. Sailesh's eyes began to water and he wailed uncontrollably. Only then did Shasrtiji relent. He spun his rotund body with surprising agility to face me.

'Ghandiji was hit many times and what he do?'

'Nothing. He didn't retaliate. He said it is wrong to fight violence with violence. He preached *ahimsa*.' It struck me that Shastriji was not a follower of Ghandi as he appeared to enjoy aggression, but I kept my thoughts to myself.

'So, don't ever hit anyone.' He jerked his thumb towards Sailesh. 'If you have a problem with him, you tell me and I will sort it out. Do you understand?'

I nodded.

Despite my throbbing earlobe I was delighted to have come away relatively unharmed, compared to my enemy. My joy was short-lived as a glowering *Ba* confronted me later that day.

'Why did you attack Sailesh?'

'He attacked me first.'

'He says you attacked him and got him into trouble with Shastriji.'

'That's not true.'

I was given a severe lecture and because my protests were long and loud *Ba* decided a new threat was needed to improve my behaviour. Now there were no *sadhus* to abduct me she invented new bogeymen to strike terror into my heart:

'Do you hear those drums?'

'Yes.'

'Those are the natives in the jungle. They do that when they eat bad children.'

'Eat them? How can they eat them?'

'They throw them into a giant pot and boil them until they are soft enough to eat. They come round every week looking for naughty children and take them away. You must always behave or you will end up as dinner. Believe me, they are far worse than *sadhus*.'

'Do Chikondi and Mwala eat people?'

'No, of course not. It's just the people in the jungle with the drums. So never, never, never cross the ditch and go through the trees or you will not come back.'

The joy at losing the *sadhus* was over. Now I would never cross the road.

# Chapter 13

## The soothsayer

I had seen him at the edge of our village, by the derelict land, sitting cross-legged with a white cloth in front of him to match his white *dhoti*. Spread out on the cloth were colourful charts showing the stars and planets and two gigantic dice, blank and red on some sides and white with dots on others. On one side he had a large wooden box, which was open. Inside the lid was an exultant Hanuman flying across the skies to rescue a relieved *Rama* as the demon *Ravana* looked on in anger. The man was not terrifying, like a *sadhu,* because his face was not painted. His hair was short and neatly combed back like *Bapuji's* and he wore no beads. He looked commonplace; but his prophecy would change my life.

We had lived in Nzuka for almost two years when Bapuji took me to see the soothsayer one sultry Saturday. We had settled in well and had come to regard Africa as our home. We did not really mix with local people, but whenever I met them they were kind and friendly and most had a ready smile. Once *Ba* became convinced that Africa was as safe as India we children roamed the village unsupervised. There were trees to climb and streams to wade in and dam. We played *gili danda*, marbles and card games all day long without getting bored. If we felt hungry or thirsty we would simply visit one of our neighbours' houses and be given whatever we wanted.

Out eating habits had changed, subtly. There was a shop which sold all manner of Gujarati food, including aubergines, *lilva*, okra and *gram* flour. The famous Gujarati *thali* was our staple diet until, one unforgettable day, *Ba* introduced us to exotic foreign cuisine. She came home bearing two metal tins, a large rectangular package and a smaller cylindrical one, all wrapped in thick paper. These, she announced, would be the ingredients of our first-ever English meal. She demonstrated how you opened the tins with a fancy gadget she called a 'tin opunu'.

Kumud and I examined the contents, a kind of orange-yellow mush which exuded a pleasant enough, though bland, aroma. *Ba* then made a *vagar,* which involves frying mustard and crushed coriander seeds at a high temperature in oil, until they start to pop. The smell makes you cough and splutter and the kitchen uninhabitable, but we were inured to it by now. She added chopped garlic, chillis and ginger to the mix. As soon as everything was at full sizzle she dumped the contents of the tins into the pan and threw in turmeric, *jeera* and lime juice. As it all came to the boil she strewed chopped coriander on top.

Now she opened the large packet, revealing white rectangular slices with a brown edging. She then unwrapped the small one, which contained something solid. It looked like a wodge of yellow *ghee* and was melting gently in the heat. This she spread on the white slices and we were ready to eat. *Ba* slopped *raita*, lime and mango pickles on our plates, brought over a plateful of grilled *poppadums* she had carefully carried all the way from India, then gave us a generous helping of the tinned delicacy.

'Bakid binz and *vagar*,' she proclaimed proudly. 'This is what the English eat when they cannot get meat. They are lazy and do not make fresh *chapattis* every day. Instead they buy these white things they call 'slaycid brid' and they put this thing called 'booter' on it. It's very nice, like *ghee*. I tried some in the shop.'

Baked beans with buttered bread instantly became our favourite foreign meal and we clamoured for it often. More English delicacies followed. There were rectangular blocks of soft yellow *kulfi* held together by two biscuits, which we called 'eyes crem' and a red soup, similar to *dhal,* which tasted of tomatoes and nothing else. We tried this heated straight from the tin à *l'anglais* but were unimpressed, until *Ba* added a *vagar* and spices. It was delicious with buttered bread, chilli pickle and *poppadums*. I pitied the poor English and wondered how they survived on their bland fare.

Over the months even Sailesh became a friend, though I kept a wary eye on him. We vied to be top of the class and once ended with equal marks for the whole term, which had never happened before. Our parents were as competitive as we were, urging their respective sons on to beat the rival. I enjoyed school and was never bored. Shastriji was strict but amusing, a perfect combination, I thought, for an authority figure. The teaching was almost identical to that in Ganeshgam: we did a lot of reading, writing and maths and very little else. The reading was usually simplified tales from holy books like the *Ramayna* and the *Mahabharata* and Indian history.

*Bapuji* was disappointed that we were not learning Sanskrit, as he had at my age, but delighted that we were beginning English lessons. Within a few weeks I could tell any English person who might be interested that 'the cat sat on the mat', 'it is fun to run in the sun' and 'the dog barks at the fog'. I had no idea what fog was so I asked Shastriji, who explained that it was a big cloud which came down to earth so that you could see nothing, not even your hand in front of your face. Apparently this happened a lot in England which seemed a dark and dismal place, full of snow and dense fogs, where people perpetually stayed indoors, not venturing outside. I learned that it also rained there almost every day and not just in the monsoon season. The story book illustrations showing men in odd-looking striped outfits and circular black hats, invariably carrying umbrellas, reinforced my view that it was not a place worth visiting. The women looked peculiar too. They wore garments which did not reach the floor, as *saris* did, and often had very short hair so that they looked like men. I was struggling to understand why we were learning their language and not something useful, like Swahili.

A cinema named 'Jyoti', after the owner's daughter, had opened in the centre of Nzuka, showing Hindi films. Hindi and Gujarati are similar but sufficiently different that I could understand only about a third of what was going on. In India I would have been taught the national language at school, but here there were no Hindi lessons. I struggled to grasp whatever we were watching and often fell asleep after finishing my Fanta and bag of kips. By now I could read 'Fanta' on the label, but couldn't get my tongue round the printing on the packet: 'potato crisps'. The words were too long and difficult and I wondered why the spelling was not simply 'kips'. Shastriji would know. I stuck an empty packet in my pocket so that I could ask him.

One Friday evening we went to the European cinema, the Roxy, to see a film in English, *Journey to the Centre of the Earth*. I concentrated hard but couldn't work out much of the dialogue. The characters intrigued me: their clothes, their mannerisms appearance. It was a revelation that there were so many shades of hair colour other than black. I thought eyes were always black or brown. Here, in full Technicolour on the giant screen, hair was often chestnut, red or even yellow and eyes were sometimes green and blue. Even though I didn't understand the plot, the action enthralled me and the lack of persistent and inconsequential song-and-dance made every frame exciting. I decided there and then to pay more attention in English lessons.

It was the following morning that we sat down with the soothsayer. We faced him with our legs likewise crossed and *Bapuji* gave him the requisite amount of *kwachas.* The soothsayer beamed as he stashed the cash in his top pocket. This would buy us an hour of his valuable time. He wanted to know my date, time and place of birth and my full name. He examined the palms of my hands and made some notes. Then he produced a book from his magic box and ran his fingers down the relevant pages until he found the vital data. He consulted the charts before him, which were covered in flowing circles, lines and squiggles, and asked questions about my likes and dislikes. After each reply he threw the dice and jotted down the results.

He flaunted a flimsy eight-page booklet. It had dozens of small red swastikas around the edge and a sketch of *Ganesh* in the middle. Underneath *Ganesh* I could make out the word *'janmotri'.* The contents, yet to be written, would be my horoscope. All Hindus who can afford it visit a soothsayer so that their lives are clearly mapped out and they can safely navigate their journey, sure of the destination. The poor are condemned to face the future without a clue to the pitfalls and joys coming their way. During the next few minutes my prospects would be written out baldly in blue ink and these words would guide me through the following decades, assuming no early demise was forecast.

The soothsayer hummed and chanted as he worked, drumming his fingers on the cloth, occasionally asking questions about *Ba* and *Bapuji's* dates and places of birth and scribbling in the booklet in between. Surprisingly quickly his calculations were complete and he revealed that I was born on a Friday, an auspicious day, and that the star signs had revealed the letter 'b', which was why I was named Bharatkumar. This much *Bapuji* already knew so he asked what more he could tell us.

The soothsayer sat up straight and read out what he had written.

*'Janmotri Bharatkumar Dahyabhai Patel, born in Ganeshgam, district Valsad.*

*'Bharat will be happy throughout his life and educated to the highest standard. However, he will be forced to travel far, far away to achieve this. He will visit many countries and see many things. When he is 21 he will leave education or else continue until he is 25 and after that he will earn lots of money and have a long and healthy life. He will have a special interest in music and play many instruments beautifully. He will be famous for his melodious singing. Wherever he goes, he will never be far from his family and he will look after his parents, his own children and even his relatives. He will marry at eighteen, or at twenty-five. He will choose his own partner and love her dearly and they will be most happy together and have at least two healthy and happy children. He will impart his great knowledge to his friends. He will have lots of cars and enjoy them tremendously. His karma says he will achieve the very best and will keep striving until he does so.*

'One more thing. I very much recommend you buy a copy of this book'. He picked up a heavy yellow tome with red titles. 'It is *Cheiro's Book of Numbers*, a most famous book which will steer you throughout your life. It is full of advice on improving your fortune. It also has much wisdom.'

We left shortly afterwards, *Bapuji* toting his expensively-acquired and very heavy book. For days afterwards he immersed himself in it, his brow furrowed, making copious notes. He told me that Cheiro was a great man who had predicted many things. He came from Ireland, a country near England. He had studied with a *Brahmin* in Mumbai and met many notable men and women whose future he foretold, among them Mark Twain, Mata Hari, Oscar Wilde and the British prime ministers Gladstone and Chamberlain. He explained who they all were, but the names meant nothing to me. I was more interested in his predictions.

'Well, as an example, he told the future king of England, the Prince of Wales, that he would never be crowned because he would give up everything for the love of a woman he was forbidden to marry. This is *exactly* what happened.'

'Why was he forbidden to marry?'

'It is complicated. It is the forecast and outcome that are important and he was absolutely correct. Also, there are people called Jews who were driven out of their country two thousand years ago. You are seven, so imagine how long two thousand years is. During that time they have lived all over the world, but they wanted to return to their own country, which is called Palestine. They always remembered they were Jews and they prayed to get their land back. Well, Cheiro said it would happen very soon and it did! So, you see, he was a very great man. He could not possibly have known all these things yet somehow he used numbers to work out what would happen.'

*Bapuji* had already made an important discovery. According to Cheiro's system my name was unlucky.

'Cheiro gives every letter a number, so you can add up the letters of your name to see if it comes to a lucky number. Your name comes to a *most* unlucky number and we cannot have that. I must act as soon as possible because very soon I will be getting you a passport, which is a little book with your photo inside. You need to have it with you whenever you go from one country to another and it will have your name written in English. So we will change it.'

'Will I no longer be Bharat?'

'No, no. You will still be Bharat, but there will be an extra letter in your name which will not change the pronunciation. It is quite easy to do in English. Now I must work out what that extra letter is.' With this he vanished behind Cheiro.

A month later B*apuji* went to the capital city, Lusaka and two days later he returned, triumphantly waving three passports.

'These are British passports. I already have one and so now do you all. It means we can travel anywhere in the world without a problem. A British passport is far better than an Indian one. Also, I have successfully changed your name. You are now Bharatkumaar, so you have an extra 'a' in your name which makes it very lucky indeed.' He spelt it out letter by letter and made me write it down. 'You have gone from misfortune to great fortune. You will see.'

I gazed at my name in wonder. It contained only six letters in Gujarati but in English it had twice as many, which made me feel important.

*Bapuji* said he had something else to tell me, which would come as a shock. *Bhulima* was not well and she felt lonely and sad. She needed someone to look after her, so *Ba* would be going home to India with Kumud. I would stay with him because of what was foretold in my *janmotri*.

'You remember the soothsayer predicted you would have a very good education but would have to travel far to find it?'

'Yes.'

'A good education is not possible in India or Africa. If you are to become a doctor or an engineer then you must go to university, which is a place of high learning where only the cleverest people go. The best universities are in England. Indeed, the finest education you can get in the whole world is in England. They are famous for it.'

'So we are going to England?'

'No. You are going alone. *Nana* has gone to live in a place called Leicester and you will stay with him and he will look after you. I have a good job here. I have to continue to earn money and as soon as I have enough *Ba* will join me and we will all come to England. It will be not be too long before that happens, so you must be brave and not worry. England is a wonderful country, a land of opportunity where you can become anything you want to be. It is written in your *janmotri*. But it will only happen if we take steps to make it happen.'

'Why can't we all go together later?'

'Because if you stay here too long you will learn only a little English with Shastriji. The best way to learn English is to live with the English. You must speak it all day, read it every day and listen to it all the time. That means you must go to an English school as soon as possible. In England there is an important exam called the Eleven Plus. If we delay and you only arrive in England when you are ten or eleven you will not pass it, because you will not understand the questions. If you stay here, the soothsayer's prophesies won't be realised because your English won't be good enough. Do you understand?'

I did not but nodded anyway. I was quite tearful at the prospect of my family being split across the globe and even more so at the start of the school holidays when *Ba* left with a sobbing Kumud in her arms to make the return journey by van, ship and taxi to Ganeshgam. 'I will be back soon,' she shouted through the window. 'Make sure you keep away from those drums!'

*Bapuji* said he needed three hundred English pounds to send me to England and pay *Nana* for my keep. That amounted to an awful lot of *kwachas* and it would take him some time to raise them.

Life without *Ba* for the first time in my life was very strange. Hemakaki became my surrogate mother, fussing around me and making sure I was never hungry. She failed in her duty only once, when she went to visit relatives in a nearby town and was delayed when they ran out of petrol. Chikondi and Mwala had disappeared and I came back after playing all day to find the house empty and locked, which had never happened before. The banana and pineapple trees were loaded with unripe fruits and only the chilli plant showed anything edible. I didn't hesitate. I picked several dozen chillis and ate the lot, though the odd one was so hot it made my eyes water. Hemakaki returned to find me with red streaks across my face and asked me what I had been eating. When I told her she simply could not stop laughing.

'You are a very strange boy,' she said.

A few days later she found me eating lemon halves, including the peel, sprinkled with chilli powder, a delicacy *Bhulima* adored. 'You are most strange,' she said. 'Most, most, *most*; but very funny.'

Letters from *Ba* arrived every three or four weeks and one day a telegram was delivered which made *Bapuji* very happy. I now had a baby brother, Ramesh, and photographs were in the post. They duly arrived and though *Bapuji* was wreathed in smiles, I was unimpressed. I had never seen pictures of a baby who did not look ugly and strange and these were no different.

I wanted to know all about *Ba* and about *Bhulima*'s health and after some brief answers *Bapuji* had a question for me: would I like to see another jiruf? I told him I was desperate to see one. As we lived in a large city, even with a forest nearby we rarely saw wild animals. You would occasionally spot monkeys scampering through the branches of a tree or find an odd buffalo slumbering by the roadside. And a hyena regularly visited our house and waited patiently for Mwala, because he always fed him meat. Chikondi was scared of the hyena and kept well away.

*Bapuji*'s shop was sending him to a town near the Zimbabwe border for what he called a 'business meeting'. These two words belonged to a group which seemed to have no direct translation into Gujarati and were slipped into conversation as if they naturally belonged. The most common were 'city centre' 'kips', 'van', 'tin', 'bakid beanz', slaycid brid' and 'booter'.

Jagdishkaka would be our safari driver. A few days later the three of us set off along the usual lumpy bumpy roads, the boot loaded with *tiffin, samosas, chevro* and *puris.* To my disappointment we first visited an ugly town where *Bapuji* disappeared for hours while Jagdishkaka did his best to keep me entertained, supplying me with *kulfis* and sweets. The next day we were back on the long road and I had just dozed off when I was awoken by *Bapuji* shouting, '*Hathi, Hathi. Bo mota hathi, ta jow!'* 'Elephants, elephants, great big elephants, look over there!' To our left was a herd of elephants far bigger, as *Bapuji* had predicted, than Indian ones. They were polishing off the last leaves of a tree before moving on to the next one.

It wasn't just their size which transfixed me: there was something odd about their appearance. Eventually I realised what it was. Their ears were huge, almost out of proportion to their bodies. Mimi, our village elephant, was dainty in comparison. These elephants were also more wrinkled. Perhaps that was because they were older.

One of them spotted our van and ambled over to take a closer look. Half a dozen began to follow and clouds of red dust reared up as they sped up and charged towards us. Jagishkaka slammed his foot on the accelerator and drove fast for a couple of miles until they disappeared from view.

Our relief was short-lived. We soon spotted a group of baboons and stopped to photograph them. *Bapuji* opened a window for a clearer picture and a baboon jumped effortlessly in. He sat on *Bapuji's* lap and gazed at him, as a child might look at its mother. For a few seconds *Bapuji* was too stunned to say or do anything, then he screamed in sheer terror, piercing my eardrums. He shoved the baboon away, opened his door and shot out, ran round the van to the back door and dragged me out too. Jagdishkaka had leapt from the driver's seat and we found ourselves facing a couple of dozen baboons, all grunting and barking excitedly and waving their arms about.

Both *Bapuji* and Jagdishkaka seemed petrified, yet I felt strangely calm. The baboon inside the van helped himself to a bag of samosas, jumped out with it and sat gazing at us defiantly. After a second we all three threw ourselves back inside the van and drove away as fast as we could. Jagdishkaka began chortling uncontrollably.

'Those baboons will find Hemakaki's samosas too hot to handle and they will realise you shouldn't mess with human beings. We don't want them bothering us again, so I must give you both a warning. Please do not open any more windows when we stop, however hot it gets.'

It was a full hour before we saw any giraffes. There were about ten of them, chomping at trees in pairs and thankfully paying not the slightest attention to their prying visitors. We sat and watched them for a long time from the safety of the van, windows shut, chewing on our *chevro* rations and sipping another drink I had found in Africa, Coca Cola. In the distance I saw what I assumed was a striped horse. It was smaller than any I'd seen before, but its black and white stripes were mesmerising. I decided it was the most beautiful creature I had ever seen.

'Like the jiruf, we don't have a Gujarati word for that horse', said Jagdishkaka. 'The English call it a jibroo.' I studied its mouth but could detect no curling of the lower lip and wondered why it had been given such a strange name. Perhaps it pulled a *jibroo* when it was sad.

We returned to Nzuka and the months passed in a slow heat haze until at last *Bapuji* reached his financial target. One day when I returned from school he was waiting for me outside the house, clutching tickets for my passage to England. He raised his head and stared intently at the sky.

'Look!' He pointed. 'You will be flying in one of those high up in the clouds, all the way to England.'

I had seen my first aeroplane above Ganeshgam, when I ran into the house to tell Bhulima there was a giant bird in the sky.

'It is not a bird, it is a *viman*,' she said. 'It looks like a bird but it is as big as our house and full of people: as many as two hundred. *Vimans* go very fast: faster than a jackal and ten times faster than any car. They take people all over the world, very very quickly. You will fly in a *viman* one day.'

'How does it stay up?'

'*Hanuman* sends his helpers to keep it up in the air. You cannot see them, but they are there, holding it up and moving it swiftly across the skies.'

Now I looked up at the flying house and imagined I could see a battalion of Hanumans below, keeping it from falling. I was thrilled at the notion of being magically transported by gods, yet at the same time sad because I loved Africa and doubted I would like the cold, wet, foggy, snow-bound country about to become my new home. The natives with bowler hats and umbrellas seemed to be an alien species, far more bizarre than Africans, Muslims or Sikhs. They lived like hermits, not venturing out whether it was hot or cold. Bapuji said they had ruled half the world and once their empire was bigger than the Mughals'. I was struggling to understand how.

# pudding

*England is my home and I embrace almost all its customs. English tea, without masala; Sunday roasts; fish and chips, occasionally enlivened by a dollop of chilli sauce; a pint in the pub; queuing politely without complaint while grumbling under my breath; constantly remarking on the weather, stating the bleeding obvious. All these are, for me, routine.*

*Imagine a boy of eight who had only seen a few white people in a crowded African street and on screen in just one film, whose experience of 'English' food is Coca Cola, Fanta, crisps and baked beans; whose English is limited to cats sitting on mats, landing at Heathrow Airport. He can only describe what he sees and hears and some of his ideas may now be outrageous.*

*Even after Windrush there were few African-Caribbeans on the streets and the Ugandan Asian influx was a few years away. Just like me, my classmates, teachers and neighbours had rarely had a close encounter with a foreigner. Ill-informed and unaware, we were all mired in prejudice and preconceptions. We circled like dogs, sniffing the mysterious tangs emanating from one another and learning about our differing customs. Gradually we realised we were not that dissimilar.*

*It took a while. This is an account of that perplexing period when children of all colours and creeds happily collected golliwogs produced by a jam manufacturer and one of the nation's favourite TV programmes was* The Black and White Minstrel Show, *in which white entertainers painted their faces black, drew rings around their eyes and daubed on white lips, fixed in grotesque grins.*

*We have come a long way, but to understand our current destination we need to understand the journey.*

# Chapter 14

## The big boy in the cot

I had left a continent of small elephants and discovered large ones in another. I had hopes the trend would continue. Even the elephants had been outstripped in height by giraffes and in beauty by zebras.

At Heathrow I saw the largest animal I would regularly spot in my new homeland: a snarling Alsatian. Living in the inner city it would be eighteen months before I encountered the big beasts of England: the horse and the cow. And there was another downgrade: the size of my bed.

The room was small, about twelve feet square, much of it occupied by the small double bed where *Nani* and *Nana* slept, just about leaving room for two suitcases to store clothes in and a cot. The cot was sturdy and quite delightful for a two or even a three-year-old, but not for a fast-growing boy of eight.

It had a plastic mattress so that discharges from either end of a baby could be easily wiped away. The pillow, with its red and yellow roses, was incongruously large and bulky, occupying a third of the sleeping zone. I climbed in, clutching my curious hot water bottle, lay down on my side with my legs bent double and pulled the blankets over my head. After a long night of contortions and thrashing about I woke with stiff aching knees. I yearned for *Hanuman's* power of changing size so that I could fit neatly inside my barred prison. I would write to *Bapuji* and ask him to send a return ticket; but for the moment my only recourse was ardent prayer. '*Ram*, why have you brought me to this place? *Please* take me back home. *Ram, Ram, Ram...*'

My journey to Leicester had begun with expectation and trepidation. I was looking forward to exploring a new foreign land, but terrified I might hate it. At the airport *Bapuji* tried to calm my qualms.

'You must be brave. Where you are going there are lots of people called 'Scots' and they are known as 'Bravehearts'. They fear nothing, not even the snow and the cold; so aim to be like them. And remember, when a bird is born it is afraid because it cannot fly or find food and has to stay with its parents in the nest. One day it must learn to fly, otherwise it will never be able to feed itself. This is the moment to spread your wings and soar away like that baby bird. And the Scots.'

I was handed over to two air stewardesses who were my minders on the five-thousand-mile flight from Nzuka to London, via Cairo, Rome and Paris. I boarded the BOAC plane as a VIP, courtesy of some string-pulling by *Bapuji's* employer, Mr Robinson, who had a puzzling amount of influence. Apparently he was a 'mason'. I had no idea what that was; only that Mr Robinson knew important people and I would be extremely well looked after.

The stewardesses were oddly attired. Their legs were bare, uncovered by *saris*. I had never seen a woman's legs in the flesh before, apart from the ones belonging to Bhulima and *Ba*. Most striking of all, they had bright red colouring on their lips. At first I assumed they had been chewing a lot of *paans,* but soon realised they had painted the red on, like henna. Both had yellow hair and blue eyes, which I found fascinating. I wanted to stare at them all the time. I knew it was rude, so I stole a glance whenever I could, hoping they didn't notice.

A tall man in a flat cap with gold stripes around it emerged from the cabin and they introduced him to me as 'the Captain'. I greeted him with *'Jaisi Krishna'*, but he looked baffled and held out his hand. Seeing that the ritual was strange to me he picked up my arm, placed my hand in his and shook it vigorously. 'You must say "Hello" when you meet someone. This is how we greet people in England.' Here were a couple of words I recognised so I replied, 'Hello, how are you? Well, I hope.'

He laughed, said something I didn't understand and handed me a badge emblazoned with the letters 'BOAC'. He pinned it to my newly-acquired navy blue jumper, along with a printed sticker identifying me as Captain Bharatkumaar Patel. According to *Bapuji* my jumper, made of the finest acrylic and nylon, was essential for surviving the English cold. I hoped England would be warmer than the air-conditioned cabin. The stewardesses soon noticed that I was shivering and carefully wrapped me inside a BOAC blanket.

Throughout the flight these colourful creatures treated me like a *pukka* prince and I began to enjoy myself. Food and drink arrived at regular intervals and one of my courtiers even accompanied me to the toilet. I examined it with interest. It was raised high above the ground and looked most uncomfortable. It was much smaller than the hole in the ground I was accustomed to and I assumed it had been reduced to this because of the lack of space in the aircraft. I decided I didn't like it. There was no jug, so I had to hold water in my cupped left hand to wash myself, which created a wet mess on the floor that took several minutes to clear up. The stewardess waiting outside became concerned and knocked, asking if I was okay. This was another word I knew. 'Okay, okay. Very good, Madam,' I replied in my best English. 'One minute, please.'

The stewardesses sat with me whenever they could. We played cards and they produced a game which involved throwing dice, sliding down snakes and climbing up ladders. After twice slithering down the longest snake when close to victory, I decided a strategically-placed mongoose or two would improve their peculiar pastime. But our conversation was limited and they had duties to perform. It was during one of these periods, somewhere between Cairo and Rome, that I began to feel melancholy and very alone. The stewardesses soon sensed I need cheering up and ushered me into the cockpit to let me fly the plane. For a few moments I really believed that, aided by Hanuman's monkey squadron, I was steering all the passengers to their destination. I wondered whether I was the youngest pilot in the history of the world. The excitement promoted a long and very deep sleep and I awoke as we landed with a jolt and a judder at London

Heathrow.

With a stewardess holding each hand I was guided through customs, where a man in uniform saluted me and clicked his heels together. He examined my sticker intently and said, 'Welcome to England, Captain Barrat-come-arr.' It took me a few seconds to realise he was saying my name. The only English words I could think of were 'Hello, how are you. Well, I hope?' which I produced staccato, stressing each one. 'I am very well, thank you, Captain,' he replied. 'I trust you had a comfortable journey.' This last remark was incomprehensible, so I smiled benignly and walked on.

At last we emerged into the arrivals hall and there, on the other side of the rope barrier, stood the familiar figure of *Nana,* nodding amiably at me. Beside him was *Fouaji*, who was married to *Bapuji's* younger sister, Laxmi. I had never met him but recognised him from a photograph we had at home. At first I thought *Fouaji* had two heads. Close inspection revealed a hood sitting up behind his face, attached to a bulky coat which had wooden pegs instead of buttons.

We went outside to the parked car and the huge drop in temperature made me shudder like the plane. This was far chillier than the cabin. *Nana* took off his huge coat, wrapped it twice around me, laughing at my forlorn face. 'We will buy you warm clothes tomorrow. You will need a doofal cott like *Fouaji's* because they keep you warm and dry.' It was the first time he had spoken and the words set off a bout of coughing. I was taken aback because I was familiar with his voice and now the tone was dramatically different. All the sounds seemed to be coming out of his nose, like an elephant. I would have understood if he had been pinching it as he spoke, but both hands were by his sides.

'What has happened to your voice, *Nana*?'

He burst out laughing, and even that sounded peculiar.

'I have what the English call a 'cold'. It means I am a bit ill, but not enough to stop me doing things. You sneeze and cough like a monkey. Everyone here suffers from colds, especially when the weather is bad like at this time of year. It will go away in a day or two.'

This was my introduction to the world of English ailments. We had cholera, typhoid, malaria and hepatitis, but nobody I knew had ever suffered from a 'cold'.

I was tired and dejected and my uncles tried to distract me. They put on their jolliest faces and chattered all the way home, asking about Nzuka and *Bapuji* and *Ba* and the rest of the family as we sped up the M1. They maintained it was the finest and fastest road in the world and it certainly felt smoother than the roads in Zambia. There, if you drove at any speed you risked becoming airborne as you hit the succession of potholes. It was a strange sensation: anticipating jolts and lurches and gliding along serenely instead.

I asked *Nana* about my new home city and he said it was big, but not as big as Mumbai. There were no farms so he had experimented with several trades and was now working in an engineering factory, but his first job was a stint down a mine. I had no concept of mining, so he plunged into a detailed account of the long dangerous journey underground to dig up coal. It reminded me of the *Journey to the Centre of the Earth* screening in Africa. I didn't know what coal was, so *Nana* promised to show me some.

When we arrived I was led though a small shop selling Indian groceries and tobacco. *Nani,* who was at the counter serving a man with cigarettes, smiled broadly, gave me a quick hug and said she'd be with us in a minute. Behind a narrow door was the living room. Fading light, entering through the four panes of a small window held together by rotting wood, was just enough to make out three people huddled inside: *Bapuji's* sister, *Foy,* and her two children, Anil and Mahendra.

The room was piled high and wide with boxes, tins, flour bags, dried pulses, cigarettes, oil drums and crates of fruit and vegetables. There were no chairs: just a couple of stools placed where there were a few spare inches. *Nana, Fouaji* and I, and shortly afterwards *Nani,* made the space yet more cramped and uncomfortable.

*Nani* had recently arrived from Zimbabwe to marry *Nana.* She noticed that I was shivering even indoors and ushered me to the blazing fire, which was the only source of heat in the house. *Nana* pointed at the bucket containing unevenly-shaped black balls. 'Look, coal: the stuff that's burning. It grows deep under the earth and you have to dig it out and bring it up to the surface. This is what it looks like before you burn it: black, not red. Don't touch, it's very dirty.' I held out my hands before the fire and announced that I was hungry.

*Nani* quickly rustled up my favourite meal, baked beans with *vagar,* accompanied by *chapattis* and *poppadums*, and I washed them down with a new delight, Lucozade. She produced a jar of the first chilli pickle I had ever seen which was not homemade. I noticed that the *chapattis* were made out of orange flour – indeed, the entire meal was neon orange; yet I loved it. Here, on a stool in front of a roaring fire, I was eating my beloved exotic comfort food with the best pickle I had ever tasted, a crate of aubergines as my table.

The light swiftly faded and it was dark well before five o'clock. I was used to twelve hours of daylight and twelve of darkness, so this early gloom was a shock to me. I asked where the toilet was and, armed with a milk bottle filled with water, *Nani* led me through the tiny kitchen and out into the freezing back yard, where she switched on an outside light. The legendary fog of England had descended and visibility was down to a few feet, but I was disappointed to find no dog barking at it, as my English textbook had promised. Even with limited visibility it was obvious we were in an unlovely space, teeming with weeds and debris. Attached to the kitchen was a brick outhouse, tall and thin.

*Nani* pulled a string, which somehow lit a bulb hanging bare from the ceiling. It emitted minimal brightness, just enough to display half a dozen sleepy spiders and a strange ivory contraption which looked like a stool: a larger version of the one on the plane. I had been hoping for something more Indian.

She lifted the lid to reveal a deep hole with water sitting at the bottom. Floating on top were two thin saffron-coloured cylinders surrounded by hundreds of black specks. The sides were stained a malevolent yellow-brown, like a demon's teeth, and the outhouse stank of something strange yet familiar. The smell was not faecal, but I found it disturbing and turned up my nose.

'Oh, don't worry about that. I'm afraid we share the yard and the toilet with the family next door and the woman throws her tea leaves down there. She smokes too and her cigarette stubs end up in the water. I keep telling her, but she always leaves the toilet in a mess. Don't look alarmed, she's very nice.'

*Nani* reached up and pulled a metal chain. Water rushed down into the bowl and the debris magically disappeared. I realised that I should have done the same on the plane instead of leaving everything to slowly disappear into the ground, as we did in India and Africa.

'You see the paper hanging on the wall? The English don't use water; instead they use those sheets to wipe their bottoms and then throw them in there. It's disgusting, but I've brought water for you so you don't need to do that. Try not to get water all over the floor. After you finish just pull this chain and it will all disappear. Then you come inside and wash your hands in the kitchen.'

She closed the door and I examined the paper. It was similar to the sheets I had used on the plane to dry up my puddle. It hadn't occurred to me that it was for cleaning your backside. The water *Nani* gave me would have been fine, had it been warm as in India and Africa, but here the ice-cold shock was traumatising. While the rest of the family continued to use water and a bottle, it took me only a couple of days at school to become a paper convert. Carrying milk bottles into toilets was clearly not only impractical but likely to draw stares from my classmates.

But the ease of the paper was offset by its abrasive nature. It was neither soft nor luxurious and could probably be used to trace pictures. Moreover, it reeked of an obnoxious disinfectant. Every hateful roll was imprinted with the words 'Izal medicated toilet tissue' and every harsh sheet carried advice I couldn't initially understand, but which I soon added to my growing scatological vocabulary: 'Now wash your hands please'. England was not turning out to be the paradise *Bapuji* had promised and I wondered whether he had any idea of its disgraceful standards of hygiene. Surely not, or he would never have dispatched me here.

Soon it was time for bed, or in my case, cot. I arranged my legs like a grasshopper's and climbed out wearily next morning, with throbbing knees. A further shock awaited: the house had no bathroom. The procedure was to wash yourself at the kitchen sink using the contents of a kettle, heated on the gas hob, to slightly warm the Arctic water from the tap. A good Hindu has a full body wash every day, but here it would be impossible. '*Ram, Ram, Ram*, please forgive me. *Ram, Ram, Ram...*'

I was delighted to discover that the sink was not my only recourse. Every Saturday we walked a mile to Spence Street, which boasted splendid Victorian Turkish baths, steam rooms and showers. You could save ten pence by opting for the slipper baths, where you soaked in an old-fashioned tub with a high end for resting your head; towel and bar of soap included. But I wasn't keen on slipper baths because the tubs were old and dirty-looking, rimmed with yellow grime. I loved the steam rooms, because the intense heat reminded me of warmer climes and for half an hour I could revel in feeling hot and bothered again. The week's dirt would simply fall away, a shower rinsed off any remnants and I emerged gleaming; strikingly clean.

Every Saturday morning we met our friends and relatives at the baths, catching up with the week's news and arguing about football and cricket. I asked to go every day but we had neither the money nor the time. In India even the poorest Hindu bathes daily, either by immersing himself in a lake or river or using a bucket and jug. Here, bathing was a luxury for the rich.

Refreshed and sweet-smelling after my first steam and shower, I was introduced to my tea-swilling neighbour, Norah, her five children and husband, Ron, a man who walked about in the freezing cold in a string vest. I assumed he was a Braveheart. Who else would behave like that?

I had already noticed that Indians in England spoke a lot of 'Indlish', an unholy marriage of two languages. *'Ellokney beh box baked beans ne ek box cigarettes shop ma amreh joveh'* was 'They need two boxes of baked beans and a box of cigarettes in the shop right now'. *'Ajeh bo thandi che, only panch degrees'*: 'It's very cold today, only five degrees'. It took a while to connect the English word for the passageway between terraced houses, 'alley', with our concocted version: 'challey'. Possibly the initial 'ch' sound was in homage to the Prince of Wales, whose name we all knew. I learned to read and pronounce street names like 'Dale Street correctly and became badly confused when told to go to 'Del Stit.'

This strangulation of languages led to a gross error as I struggled to come to terms with English. *Nani* was speaking in Gujarati when our neighbour Norah appeared in the back yard and I assumed she was using an English noun, and not a name, when she pointed her out. *'Ta joh,* Norah *ehna garh ma thi amray avti che'*, *Nani* announced, which I thought was, 'Look, the Englishwoman is just coming out of her house'. I had no idea that Norah was a name because to me it really didn't sound like one. I similarly mistranslated 'Ron' as 'Englishman.' In the weeks ahead, as I began formulating English sentences in my head, I believed I was saying, 'I can see three Englishwomen and two Englishmen,' when I was actually claiming that I could see three Norahs and two Rons.

I learned proper Leicester dialect from my first encounter with Norah. 'Ay up, me duck, ha sit goin'? Bit parky fur yu, I bet,' was her opening remark and though I didn't understand it then I soon did, as it was her favourite greeting. She often informed me that Ron 'haz a bag on today,' or 'eez got a cobbon' which both meant that he was in a foul temper, apparently his steady state. He was often 'uptarrn' or in town, down the 'chip ole' or chip shop, wasting his money on a 'chip cob wi' bungole' which translated as a bun with chips and cheese.' She was forever offering me 'rocks', the sticky sweets which contributed to several fillings.

Norah often came into the shop to buy cigarettes and her opening gambit was usually, 'Ay up me duck, five Park Drive, only I ain't got oat. Can you stick it on tick?' *Nani* interpreted this as a request for five of the cheapest cigarettes, but sadly she was short of cash and could we put it on her growing bill? To be fair to her, she always settled it once Ron had recovered from his 'cobbon' and arrived home on Friday night with his weekly earnings.

I thought the most fascinating aspect of Norah was her legs. Not that they were objects of beauty or art; rather they were stout and uneven, like tree stumps. As with the stewardesses they were exposed and because she wore shorter skirts there was unfortunately more on view. Both legs sported a distinct brown line up the back, which I was convinced grew out of her thighs, knees and ankles. As I noticed more and more 'Norahs' with identical bulging lines I decided that all English people must bear this deformity. I suffered from this delusion until summer: the balmy day Norah appeared wearing shorts, her abnormality vanished and I learned about seams and stockings. It was a relief to conclude that the English were built like us, not marked and swollen in odd places.

But at the end of my first week I was marvelling at the deviations of my new countrymen. I was sent to visit my maternal grandmother, Gangama, and my grandfather, Morardada, who shared my late grandfather's name. They came to England at around the same time as I set sail for Africa and now lived in nearby Highfields, the poorest district of Leicester where most immigrants had settled. I had profoundly fond memories of them, and especially of Gangama. I have never met anyone as gentle or as lovable. She was no authority figure, but no one would contemplate taking advantage of her. She always dressed in a white sari and wore glasses which looked too big for her face and she was forever smiling. I think even in sleep she never switched off her happy face.

*Ba* told me about Gangama's harsh upbringing. As soon as she was old enough Gangama worked seven days a week on the family farm. She was up at dawn cooking *rotlas* and *dhal* for the *doobras* labouring in the fields and would then would trek for miles to join them in ploughing, sowing and planting until sunset, which was around half past six in the evening. Seeing her tiny frail figure it was hard to believe she had survived, so I surmised she was tougher than she looked. Morardada had rescued her from that life. She no longer needed to work and was very content.

She had prepared my new favourite meal: *bhindi bhaji* and *khadi*. Once we had eaten she said she had to go shopping and left me with her son, *Ba's* younger brother, Kishormama. Gangama always spoke softly but he had stolen all the spare vocal chords in the neighbourhood. His voice could be heard several houses away, but the redeeming feature was his constant jollity. He led me into the sparsely-furnished living room where there were no sofas, only uncomfortable folding chairs, and I sat on one of them. He asked whether I had ever seen a television and I said, 'No'. He indicated a small box in the corner.

'It's like going to the cinema, but in your own house. You can watch films and the news and all sorts of things with this. I'll show you. It takes two minutes to warm up and then you'll see pictures and hear the sound.'

The box was just over a foot in diameter, its grey-green glass front surrounded by a narrow ivory edging, with two knobs on the right. It was sitting at the centre of a small table which was about four feet high. Kishormama switched on this device, rested an arm over it and stood facing me, waiting for it to come to life. I turned my wonky chair around and gazed expectantly at the wall.

'What are you doing?'

'Waiting for the picture to come on the wall.'

'No, no, no! The picture is in here.' He jabbed his finger at the television screen.

At that moment the sound came on then the black and white picture appeared. I was transfixed. Surely this was magic! The picture was tiny and hazy, the sound quality atrocious; but it didn't matter. We had our own cinema inside the house and I was enchanted.

My first television programme was *Thunderbirds*. Kishormama struggled to translate it but explained that it was the name of the crafts I would see speeding over land and sea and even up into space. I had no idea what the characters were saying, but the action was easy to follow. It took me a few minutes to grasp that these characters were moving oddly. I had seen puppets in India but didn't make the connection and assumed that Scott Tracy, Brains and Lady Penelope were all real English people. Why they felt the need to make such elaborate jerky movements I could not fathom. Their mouths and foreheads were most peculiar and so was their manner of speaking. In *Journey to the Centre of the Earth*, I remembered, the actors were as realistic as their Indian counterparts. These were stiff and unnatural. The only conclusion I could draw was that they had to act in this way to fit inside the little box. I worried that their eyes would pop out of the sockets, so violently did they swivel from side to side as they spoke. I had little doubt they sported the worrying brown lines down the backs of their legs I had spotted on Norah and wondered what further English freakishness I would uncover. Green toenails? Stripes on their backs?

They were a strange lot. Quite unlike us.

# Chapter 15

## The secret carnivore

**O**ur shop had a fundamental flaw: it stood in a street where we were the only Indians. *Fouaji* suffered because he was a pioneer. Eighteen months later there would be dozens of Gujaratis and Punjabis and even a few Muslims within a five-minute walk, but sadly by then he had been forced to close.

Cigarettes sold well as almost everybody smoked, but there was scant passing trade for Asian groceries. *Fouaji* decided that if customers would not come to his shop, he would take his shop to them. Over a month he knocked on all known Indian doors and returned with orders from almost every one. Money was tight: often customers only wanted a pound of aubergines and a tin of *patra* and delivery was free. Some clients were almost thirty miles away in Coventry and Nuneaton, contacts of *Nana* from his stint as a miner.

Few fresh Indian goods were available. Besides our best-sellers, the aubergines, we had *bhindis*, chillis, coriander, garlic, ginger and, occasionally, mangoes. Indians borrowed cauliflowers, cabbages, carrots and beans from the local cuisine and turned them into pickles and curries;

but these were all widely available and there was no incentive to buy them from us. We stocked the full range of spices and a good selection of exotic vegetables in tins: *papri, undhiyu, karela, galora* and many more. Outselling the rest was a Bulgarian tinned *ratatouille* equivalent called *guvetch* which contained everything from aubergines to green beans. There was a hint of garlic and chilli, but *guvetch* was bland by our standards so we gave it the *vagar* treatment. To transform it into a curry we added turmeric, cumin, a dash of tamarind or lemon juice and plentiful extra chillis.

I never saw anyone English buy anything Indian or Bulgarian. To their eyes our merchandise was outlandish. They would pick up a garlic bulb or bunch of coriander, sniff it and look vexed or even disturbed before asking for ten Benson and Hedges and a box of matches.

They could have filmed *Coronation Street* here. We were surrounded by acres of back-to-back houses with neighbours traipsing in and out of each others' homes: honest working people who lived day-to-day, without plans for the following week. They smoked, drank alcohol and ate meat and we felt smug and superior simply because we did not. We heard people talking openly about 'brownies' or 'darkies', but took no offence as they seemed to be terms of reference rather than insults. There was no outward resentment or hostility. Almost all our neighbours were welcoming, curious to know where we came from and what we thought of their country. They were invariably polite and well-mannered when they came into the shop.

This friendliness, Kishormama assured me, extended to my new school. He had been a pupil there and the only foreigner in his class. His form teacher, Mrs Green, had ordered two boys to knock on his door in the evenings and at weekends, play with him and teach him English. They dutifully followed her orders, giving him no peace or respite. They even gave him spelling tests, either because they wanted to help a hapless outsider or because they were terrified of a backlash from the formidable Mrs Green. He told me I would love my school; but I was not so sure.

*Nani* escorted me to my first day of English education. Had it not been for the soothsayer I would be in Nzuka, the temperature would be more than thirty degrees Celsius and the sky cloudless. Instead it was twenty degrees colder and I was braving the famous English drizzle. Disappointingly, nobody wore a bowler hat or carried an umbrella. Instead they had donned drab grey plastic coats with hoods attached to keep them passably dry. They hurried along with their heads down and looked desolate.

It was a five-minute walk: under the forbidding railway bridge, dank and always stinking of urine; up a steep hill and past the smoking factory chimneys and a row of houses identical to ours. En route we entered a small sweetshop, setting the bell jangling. Half a dozen children filled the small space, excitedly choosing their favourites in strict turn. The sweets were new to me, but it took only a few days to memorise their names. I had never seen so many, all enticingly coloured and displayed in large glass jars. Sherbets and Parma violets became my favourites, though I had a soft spot for Dib Dabs, Wine Gummie Rolls and Curly Wurlies.

I walked through black wrought iron gates and stared in wonder. *Bapuji* had shown me pictures of English castles and my school was a red brick version, with towers climbing high and a turret. Before me was an elevated playground, accessed by half a dozen rickety steps. It was mayhem: hundreds of children cavorted about, screaming, shouting, skipping, running, pushing and shoving. It was more boisterous than anything I had encountered; yet when a teacher appeared and blew a whistle everyone stopped still like statues and marched docilely into the castle.

*Nani* handed me over to the whistle-blower, whose name was Mr Fisher. He seemed familiar and I realised he resembled an older version of the tall handsome man adorning the hoardings, advertising Brylcreem. His hair was greased and parted in the same way and he wore an identical smart blue suit. He asked me questions and when I recognised a few words I replied, 'I am very well, thank you. How are you?' He laughed and led me to my classroom, which was far warmer than our shop. I was mystified as no large fire was burning there. The heating came from a ribbed metal contraption on the wall, which gurgled and spluttered and was too hot to touch.

I was allocated a desk, looked around and everyone was staring at me. There were almost as many pupils in the class as in the two schools I had attended, combined. Unlike Kishormama, I was not the lone alien. There was a girl who was obviously Punjabi because she was wearing a *salwar kameez* and a boy at the desk next to me who looked African. He had a yellow, green and red scarf wrapped round his neck and his name was stitched into every garment in bright red: Bradford Livingstone Worrall. It seemed such a mouthful. I was grateful my own name was simpler, even after Cheiro had persuaded *Bapuji* to add the extra 'A'.

Mr Fisher took the register. He read out our names and we acknowledged our presence by shouting, 'Yes.' Hindu caste names usually reveal a person's profession, so a Chauhan or a Solanki is in the leather and shoe trade and a Patel is a merchant or a farmer. My outdated knowledge arose from two small communities in India and Africa, still largely untouched by the outside world. I was unaware that the winds of change had been blowing hard even in India, rendering caste and its related professions increasingly irrelevant.

I was keen to discover the backgrounds of my new classmates, but the only name I recognised was Jasvinder Kaur. I knew that 'Kaur' meant 'princess' because nearly every Sikh girl's name includes it. Sikh boys are usually named 'Singh', which means 'lion'. *Ba* had told me that Sikh first names can be used for both boys and girls, which was confusing. English names were even stranger.

'Aldgate.'

'Yes.'

'Beer'

'Yes.'

'Crook.'

'Yes.'

The words were new to me. I had no idea what they meant. Over the next few weeks I made a list so that I could fathom the castes of my classmates with the help of a dictionary. Most of the surnames made no sense at all. I presumed Aldgate meant 'old gate' and after deep thought came to the conclusion that these people dealt in rusty old barriers and were not to be trusted. 'Beer' was obvious, but as it was banned in the Gujarat and my family disapproved of it I decided all Beers came from a long line of alcoholics and were not respectable. Crook was definitely to be avoided as he and his family were likely to be dangerous and had probably all served time in jail.

Mr Fisher, I thought, must be similar to the malodorous *Kori* Patels, though where his family went fishing in landlocked Leicester I couldn't discover. Thankfully he did not stink, but that could be because he covered himself in the same aftershave as *Bapuji*. What the Ramsbottoms and Smellies did was anyone's guess.

I gazed at Samantha Smellie with great interest. She was by far the prettiest girl in the class. All the girls I had known had long black hair, often tied in plaits with a ribbon. Hers was a wonderful shiny yellow, short, curved like a crescent moon and upturned at the bottom. She had radiant green eyes. I was smitten.

Sadly, despite her surname, she had a problem with *my* body odour. Even though we had no bathroom I scrubbed myself thoroughly with carbolic soap every day and my hygiene was beyond reproach. The issue lay with my diet. Every day I brought in a packed lunch of two or three *chapattis* stuffed with curried vegetables and lime or chilli pickle, accompanied by pungent *poppadums* reeking of garlic and *hing*. Both my lunch and I were emitting a dire stench, mine emerging through every pore of my body at industrial strength due to the vast amount of spices I consumed.

Samantha was one of a handful who also did not eat school dinners. She brought in banana, chocolate or cheese sandwiches and was quick to show her displeasure: 'Cor, Barrat, you pong!' There were two new words here, but the way she was holding her exquisite nose left me in no doubt of their meaning. I was taken aback. She looked so perfect that I was not too angry with her and quickly forgave her for mispronouncing my name, even though I had already demonstrated the *pukka* technique.

After assembly on that first morning Mr Fisher had introduced me to the class and asked me to write my name on the blackboard. I scrawled it laboriously in chalk. He read it out, as it sounded to him.

'Baratkumar.'

'No, Bhhh-arat.' I breathed out a lungful of air to emphasise the 'h'.

'Ah, an aspirated 'b',' he said. He explained to the class what that meant. I was bewildered by what sounded like top-speed gabbling but was in fact his simple explanation to eight-year-olds.

Slowly he coaxed me into joining in and learning. In Art I drew a shockingly bad *Hanuman* and everyone was fascinated because they had never seen a monkey god before. Mr Fisher knew a surprising amount about him and grasped the opportunity to talk about his deeds and powers. When we did geography he pinned a map of India on the wall so that I could indicate my village and he used this as the starting point for a discussion of my homeland, its size, languages and religions. Using just a few words and sign language I found I could convey my thoughts and soon full and sometimes complex sentences came rushing out of my mouth.

I had no problem with maths. I could recite up to the 40 times table, so I was well ahead of even the brightest pupil. The upshot was that in English I was bottom of the class and in maths I was top, so that when the marks were totted up after the end-of-term tests I sat in twentieth place. There were forty-four in my class.

Although my English was improving fast, Mr Fisher worried about my accent and pronunciation. One afternoon he pulled me to one side, clenched his teeth and began to speak without moving them. 'Bharat, you Indians all speak with your teeth together and it makes you sound like this. It is not correct.'

Now he allowed his teeth to move apart. 'We English *enunciate*. We speak very clearly in this manner and you must do the same.' His lips were making exaggerated movements, up and down, sideways and diagonally. He reminded me of Scott Tracy in *Thunderbirds*.

All the way home I enjoyed giving my teeth and lips dramatic licence as I repeated my new mantra: 'I must *enunciate*. I must speak like the *English*, not the Indians.'

By now *Bapuji* had read my first forlorn letter about the cot, the cold, the grime and gloom of my new homeland. I received a swift reply telling me to be brave, like Robert the Bruce: 'He was a great Scottish king who fought six battles against the English and lost. As he lay in despair on his straw bed in a remote hut he saw a spider failing to swing from one wooden beam to another. The spider tried six times without success but it refused to give up and on the seventh attempt it reached the beam.

'Robert the Bruce decided to follow the spider's example, so he rose from his bed, returned to the fray and defeated the English at a place called Bannockburn. You must do likewise. I have given you a subscription to *Reader's Digest*, an excellent magazine which will teach you English and other things. Read it diligently from cover to cover and you will learn very much. *Ba* has posted some of your favourite types of *poppadums* and jars of lime pickle from India and they will arrive soon. Your ever-loving *Bapuji*.'

Even before my first *Reader's Digest* thudded through the letterbox I was reading voraciously to expand my vocabulary. Within a few months I was addicted to Enid Blyton's *Secret Seven* books and progressed through the *Famous Five*, *Adventure* and *Five Find-Outers* series until I had exhausted them all. I scoured the library shelves for Blytons but there was nothing I hadn't read, so I asked the librarian. She escorted me to a section where the books were far slimmer and I raced home, delighted with my four *Noddy* books.

'Look, Bharat's got *Noddy* books. Bharat's a baby! Bharat's a baby!' The cry went up as soon they were spotted, proudly piled on my desk. I was indignant. 'Why am I a baby?' 'Because *Noddy* is for babies.'

I hid them quickly. To me Enid Blyton was the greatest author ever to have lived, so I read them secretly at home and got to know the characters: Big-Ears, Tessie Bear, Mr Plod and the villainous gollywogs who, to my delight, were rude to that prissy Noddy and his friends and stole his car. I noticed that several of my classmates wore gollywog badges and assumed they related to the books they claimed they had outgrown. As we never ate jam or marmalade I had no idea that Robertson's, who liked to decorate their labels with gollywogs, gave badges away to loyal customers.

I had lived on three continents, speaking different languages and learning about widely-different histories and religions, so Noddy was just one of hundreds of mystifying subjects. I was well versed in the Hindu pantheon and the struggle for Indian independence, but there was a monumental gap where the reading, culture and knowledge English children acquire by the age of eight should be. *Reader's Digest* was essential in filling this void, advancing my general knowledge with articles like *The Town that Died to Live,* a two-page history of Pompeii, *The World's Greatest Musician*, a eulogy of Louis Armstrong and *The Space Race*, which detailed the contest between the USA and the USSR to be first to land men on the moon.

Each edition helped me interpret my enigmatic new land. The contrasting behaviour of my new classmates and those in Africa and India had perplexed me from the first day and the latest *Digest* dealt with violence and school bullying. As I studied the extracts from *Tom Brown's School Days* I was appalled at the brutality which seemed to be rampant in English schools. I had noticed that some children were feral and cheeky to adults to an extent I found alien. We had a culture of respect for parents and teachers and while this was true of most pupils, some were brazen in their hostility to authority and they frequently rebelled.

Discipline was rigorous and several boys were caned for their misdemeanours. More often, teachers produced a slipper and gave offenders two or three whacks across the buttocks. In Nzuka Shasrtiji had been strict, but no one he punished, with the exception of Sailesh, was keen to relive the experience. Here, miscreants merrily crossed the line again and again.

One girl, Jessie, was a frequent offender and never flinched when she was punished. Mr Fisher usually hit her on the back of her head with the palm of his hand while shouting, 'You silly lemon!' She was unfazed and I admired her greatly. She and a boy named Paul were spotted playing on the railway line by Miss Crumb, the teacher in charge of the youngest class, who reported them to the headmaster. At assembly they were called up on to the stage where the headmaster gave a long lecture on their stupidity, telling them they could have been killed, before producing the slipper. Paul burst into tears, but Jessie kept a defiant face which told everyone nothing would stop her playing roulette with the trains.

One Monday Mr Fisher was absent and for a few days a different teacher came in. We didn't like him because he was overly strict and delighted in caning anyone who misbehaved. Half the class had gone swimming when he asked the rest of us, one by one, to begin a nursery rhyme, indicating when we should all join in. I didn't know a single one and when my turn came my mind was blank. He hooked a finger and beckoned me to the front of the class where I suffered the shame of standing in the corner while the rest continued his mad rhyme game.

At the end the four of us left standing were given an hour's detention and made to copy out ten nursery rhymes. Most of them, like Humpty Dumpty and Ring a Ring O'Roses, made no sense to me. Why was a boy dressed as an egg? And what on earth were 'posies'? I quite liked Incy Wincy Spider as it reminded me of Robert the Bruce. I wondered whether the great Scot had written it.

This ignorance resulting from my upbringing dogged me for years before I finally caught up, around the time I became a teenager. Because we were vegetarian I knew little about meat and fish. One day, when we were learning about smoked fish, I was caught hook, line and sinker by Mr Fisher, who asked me why kippers were never caught off the coast of Scotland. 'Because they live in the Mediterranean?' I hazarded, to rowdy laughter. Once, in my eagerness to join in, I volunteered to defend the Ku Klux Klan in a debate, without the faintest idea about them. I had half an hour to prepare but was unable to summon up any sincere or compelling vindication of my American clients, having just discovered what they did.

My classmates' religion confused me. I simply could not understand the Christian schism between Catholics and the Church of England. Some children didn't attend assembly and I asked one, Conor, why he was always absent. After all, I was a Hindu and I attended every day. He explained that he was a Catholic and Catholics worshipped differently. He said that while both sides believe in Jesus Christ, his side thought the Pope, a very holy man, should be head of the Church, while the Protestants had opted for the Queen. 'So, Bharat, who do you think is best to lead you? The holy man, closest to God of anyone on earth, a man who studies the Bible and prays all day; or the Queen?' There seemed to be one answer.

Various sets of friends eased my assimilation into English society. Because I was obsessed with Enid Blyton I sought out two like-minded aficionados and we formed The Terrible Three. Unlike the Famous Five, the Five Find-Outers and Dog and the Secret Seven we didn't have the luxury of a shed at the bottom of the garden, so we gathered behind a pile of rubble on waste ground for our first furtive meeting. Item one on the agenda was whether or not we should wear a badge so that we could identify ourselves. I argued against this, pointing out that if we were caught and searched our badges would be discovered and our cover blown. To my surprise my suggestion of a three-fingered signal was carried unanimously. We would nonchalantly splay three fingers on a desk, waggle them in the air as if they were sore or place them on our cheeks and lean into them, as though deep in thought. Our aim was to recognise each other at all times without drawing attention to ourselves, so no one would guess we were that crime-fighting trio feared by the worldwide criminal fraternity.

Every week we watched *Police 5*, a five-minute television programme presented by Shaw Taylor, who appealed directly to the public for help solving crimes. Des, Mark and I took his appeal personally. We noted down details of suspects and car registration numbers, often with missing letters and numbers when witnesses couldn't recall them. Des had a dog, Tizer, who was co-opted into the gang, but he proved useless at following a trail. We experimented by rubbing a peeled banana across Des's lawn and urging Tizer to pursue our imaginary fruit thief. He wagged his tail, lay down and went to sleep.

Rapidly pointing a finger at each eye, Shaw Taylor always signed off with his catchphrase, 'Keep 'em peeled'. And that is exactly what we did. We lurked on street corners looking for anyone suspicious and made notes of cars with registrations vaguely similar to those driven by Shaw's dastardly villains. Badly influenced by our favourite author we scoured the streets for anyone who looked 'swarthy' or 'like a gypsy', because they were obviously 'up to no good' and followed them out of sheer boredom until they disappeared into a house or shop or hopped on to a bus. We didn't catch a single culprit. After a year the Terrible Three disbanded and the desperados of Leicester heaved a sigh of relief.

Daniel and Gianlucca, who were Polish and Italian, introduced me to the world of comics. They read the *Dandy*, the *Beano* and the *Beezer* and their heaps of back copies set off an explosion in my vocabulary. I revelled in a cornucopia of new sounds, like 'whizz!' 'chomp!' 'splot!' 'slam' 'rumble!' and 'whump!' and my familiarity with rhyme burgeoned as I read about Roger the Dodger, Beryl the Peril and Dennis the Menace.

We moved on to more expensive American comics and formed a club so that we could swap. *Captain Marvel* was our favourite and the superhero was responsible for almost hospitalising me. In real life he was Billy Batson, but had only to shout 'Shazam!' to transform into Captain Marvel and fly. I would often shout 'Shazam!, raise my right arm and soar into the skies by jumping off a three-foot wall, landing with a thud on the pavement. Then the resourceful Daniel located a derelict house with a mattress outside and we took turns shouting the magic word and jumping from the first floor window. It worked thrillingly for weeks, until the day I bounced straight off the mattress and shot at speed onto unforgiving lumpy concrete. I almost broke a leg and sat there dazed and battered, with an enormous graze across my arm.

A third set of friends took me trainspotting. We clambered up an embankment and watched the trains slowing down to pull into London Road Station. We had bought a guide with the number of every train printed inside and when we spotted one, ticked it off. I managed to stand the tedium three times before I quit to join the mob playing football on the local park. At the weekend and during the holidays a single game began at nine in the morning and ended only at dusk, with participants leaving and returning whenever they felt like it, often on the opposing side.

This constant activity and the cold, even in summer, made me ravenous.

The two-*chappatis*-and-*poppadums* diet simply didn't satisfy me, so I asked *Nana* and *Nani* if I could have school dinners. As they were free, they agreed. I didn't know how to hold a knife and fork and ate with the fork in my right hand and the knife in my left, which made everyone ask if I was left-handed.

It took some time to adapt to the blandness of school dinners. I was accustomed to heat and spices which made food tasty and joyful, but now I had replaced quality with quantity, forfeiting anticipation and flavour. There was no vegetarian option and over-boiled vegetables and thin gravy were a poor introduction to English cuisine; though even I had to admit there was some respite in apple pie and custard, treacle tart and jam roly-poly.

Driven by hunger, I persisted with my dreary diet and like a prisoner in jail slowly accepted it. I ladled on extra mustard, ketchup, mint and apple sauce whenever they appeared to make the mash and washed-out cabbage palatable. Eventually I came up with a solution: I carried a bottle of hot sauce in my pocket at all times and surreptitiously sprinkled drops over my lunches to make them more edible. Twice I was caught in the act but explained to my inquisitors that the sauce was actually a medicine for a dodgy tummy.

For the first few weeks I rejected all meat, but I freely ladled gravy over everything, not knowing it was contaminated with the flesh of animals. I also ate suet pudding as the name gave no clue to its meaty credentials. I did, however, refuse to touch any pudding which included mincemeat, as I reasoned it must be made from lamb, or even beef. I was puzzled that mincemeat was always accompanied by custard and concluded that the dinner ladies must add a lot of sugar to disguise the flavour. I was appalled that my classmates ate hot dogs. What kind of people ate dogs while pretending to be fond of them and keeping them as pets? I decided dogs were living on the edge.

Eventually my growing hunger pangs led me to eat meat; though I wouldn't touch beef as it was against my religion. I kept my new vice secret from my family, who would be horrified to discover that I was eating animals. I was slowly turning English.

Apart from the cot, I liked living in the shop, where *Nani* had become my second surrogate *Ba* after Hemakaki. She played board games with me, read to me and took me to the cinema twice a week. On Friday nights we usually saw English films but I was disappointed that they were often musicals like *Camelot, Dr Doolittle* and old Elvis films, without explosions or fighting. On Sundays we never missed the ritual Bollywood blockbuster, always full of silly song-and-dance routines.

We didn't have a television, but we knew people who did. During the week, after our evening meal, we visited various *kakas* and *kakis* so that we could watch all our favourite shows, like *Bewitched, Batman, Bonanza* and *The Saint*. Occasionally there would be a late finish, usually for Hollywood films like *Kim* and *Elephant Boy,* featuring real Indian actors. On these special nights I was marched through the streets to the viewing in my pyjamas, teeth brushed and chattering with the cold, so that I could be dispatched straight to my cot upon return.

*Nani* introduced me to new pleasures: Victoria sponge, jammy scones and freshly-baked fairy cakes with a cherry on the top. We enjoyed baking together and our bond was very close. England felt less strange every day as she helped me adapt to the fresh culture.

One moment encapsulated my new optimism. I caught her dancing alone in the kitchen to Dean Martin's *That's Amore*. She had wonderful poise and grace and her movements were familiar yet different to anything I had seen in films: a fusion of English and Indian with a touch of her own elusive style. She looked blissful in that moment. She saw me watching and made me join her and the indefinable joy of our crazy dancing was life-affirming. Suddenly I realised that I belong here. At last my yearnings for Africa and India were receding and I was happy.

# Chapter 16

## The promised land

The shop was in steep decline and it became clear that *Fouaji* was flogging a dead horse. In Indian parlance, he was attempting to offload ageing aubergines and few were buying. They lay dejected in crates, shrivelling and developing mould faster than we could eat them. A daily *brinjal bhaji* diet soon palls and it would be many years before I enjoyed them again.

The shop was sold, *Foy* and *Fouaji* moved into a terraced house nearby and we rented rooms in an edgier part of Highfields. The city council, in its limited wisdom, had put up hideous tower blocks just around the corner. They were filled with people who seemed to be at odds, relishing skirmishes and sustained slanging matches no matter the time of day or night. We were fifty yards away, but we heard their voices booming out from a dozen floors and they were kind enough to help expand my vocabulary. Soon I was conversant with 'fuck off, you slimy bastard', which added three marvellous words to my lexicon, closely followed by 'bugger', 'twat', 'crap, 'slut' and 'bitch'.

I often saw people brawling and wrestling in the street but if I did not stop and stare they usually continued their tussle without bothering me. Once I glanced up to see a large object flying though the air from a top floor and crashing close to where I was walking. It was a television, innocent victim of a battle in one of the flats. The glass shattered and plastic and metal debris shot out in a giant circle, but luckily I was unhurt. 'That'll serve you right, you fucking loony,' screamed a disembodied voice. 'Now how will you watch your bloody racing?' A fat man in a vest peered over the balcony, his face forlorn. He stuck his hand over the railing and casually dropped a green bottle. As it smashed into smithereens he roared with laughter and disappeared inside to resume the discussion.

I often had to walk around and jump over vomit and dog mess on the pavement. Once I came across a tramp with a large plastic cider bottle in his hand, squatting and defecating. Such sights were common in India and Africa, though I had never seen alcohol involved before. Here it was shocking.

At the end of the street, in the evenings, a number of women gathered to stand around chatting until passing men arrived and spoke to them. Then one by one they would disappear with the men, only to return within half an hour. I was puzzled by this behaviour, but by now the Terrible Three had disbanded and was unable to investigate the Mystery of the Disappearing and Rapidly Reappearing Women.

These women's clothes were markedly different from those worn by the mums at the school gate. They wore far shorter dresses, bright and eye-catching, red being the most popular colour. They eschewed warm coats even when it was very cold, preferring to shiver in the gales and hail than to wrap up. Indeed, they covered as little as they possibly could. I recognised one as the mother of one of my schoolmates. I had seen a dinner lady point her out and say she was 'on the game'. I had no idea what sort of game she played, though I thought it probably wasn't Snakes and Ladders.

I had at last escaped my cot and slept in a real bed. Indeed, I slept in a separate room from *Nani* and *Nana* as they now had a baby, Mukesh, who suited my old sleeping space much better. But my joy in luxuriating on a full-size mattress was short-lived as two more single beds were soon jammed into my room and I had to share with two men, both proficient in rasping snores and unexpectedly loud and extended explosions in the middle of the night. Their cheap and cheerful *dhal* and rice diet made flatulence inevitable. In reality there were three men, as my two sleeping companions worked long hours in factories and one or other of their beds was occupied by a night worker as soon as it became vacant. The beds completely filled the room, the curtains were never drawn and a stale sweaty stench hung in the air.

The house was owned by Hirakaka and Savitakaki, distant relatives from a village near Munsari. Hirakaka's default expression was harried and doom-laden, as if the world would be ending in a minute or two. He had hunched shoulders and a constant cold; ill-fitting tortoiseshell spectacles hung grimly on the end of his bulbous nose. We rarely saw him as he was invariably sorting out accounts in his room, between regular sneezing fits. Perhaps this explained the drooping glasses: buffeted by seismic forces and blown off whenever there was a colossal eruption.

He had three children, two younger than me and one much older. The house was crammed, often with standing room only in the lounge. A *carrom* board, about four feet square, was propped up against one wall and when it was laid flat on the floor it made the room yet more crowded. It resembled a small snooker table, with a pocket at each corner into which you potted the nine wooden discs. If you managed this and potted the red queen disc before your opponent, you won the game. There were no cues: you flicked the discs with your fingers and they slid around erratically because the surface was polished and liberally sprinkled with talcum powder.

Games were noisy and there were riotous disputes and the odd friendly fight. To increase the jollity we had constant visitors who popped in for no good reason and had to be plied with *masala* tea and *bhajias* or *chevro*. There was never any peace and I was driven to seek the silence I craved at the local library or at the museum. We were not given homework so I read voraciously, moving from author to author as I exhausted their output. Without realising it I was raising my English to the level necessary to pass a vital exam.

Several times a week Mr Fisher set tests, explaining in detail what we had to do, but I rarely paid attention to his pronouncements and just got on with the task before me. That is how I came to sit the Eleven Plus without knowing it, even though *Bapuji* had sent me thousands of miles for this one reason. I had never heard of grammar schools and had no idea I had worked my passage to an elite education until a few weeks later when Mr

Fisher read out the results. Fourteen out of forty-four of us would be going to grammar school, the rest to secondary moderns. Jessie, the naughty girl, passed the exam and so did Samantha; but she chose to go to the local secondary modern with her friends. Mr Fisher was furious, telling her she was giving up the most important opportunity of her life, but she would not be dissuaded.

Three days later, as the sun was setting, there was a knock at the door. A salesman was outside who persuaded *Nana* to part with a week's wages in exchange for a set of books to steer me though the next stage of my life. Without these, he said, I would struggle to keep up with the hard work ahead. Armed with them, I would have a head start on my new classmates. These pearls of wisdom continued for an hour until *Nana* signed on the dotted line.

The books were beautifully bound in claret leather with gold lettering and there were fourteen of them, titled Mathematics, French, German, English, Science, Geography, History, Law, Sociology, Economics, Design, Art, Music and Religion. I looked for Indian history but it was nowhere to be found, though there were chapters on the American Civil War and the Russian Revolution. I probably referred to my new library a dozen times, never finding what I was looking for, and eventually abandoned them to a high shelf to gather dust.

My best friend Daniel had failed the test. By now I had grasped that it was important and that some of my friends were crestfallen. When I went round to his house I heard his dad yelling at him. I had never seen him before but knew he came from Katowice in Poland, which Daniel said was uglier and smellier than Leicester, which seemed unlikely.

'If you'd done your homework like I told you and stopped reading those bloody comic books you'd have gone to grammar school. You're a clever lad and you've blown your one and only chance. You'll end up in a sodding factory, like me.'

He spotted me walking past the window.

'Who's that?'

'My friend Bharat.'

'He's a darkie. Why are you friends with a darkie?'

I fled. The following day Daniel told me to forget his dad and only come round when he was at work. His mum always made me welcome and plied me with satisfying Polish dishes. She cooked a fabulous *bigos* which I loved because it was crammed with spicy sausage and always kept a store of *paczki,* round spongy cakes with a strawberry and rose filling.

A boy with striking red hair and a pock-marked face, like a character in the *Beano*, lived a few doors away from Daniel. Whenever he saw me he stared and stuck out his tongue and one day he followed me down the street shouting, 'Paki!' I ignored him, until the next edition of *Reader's Digest* – by now my guide to western living – arrived, featuring an article headed, Confront your Fear and Anger. This gave fulsome advice on what to do in times of difficulty and stress and one of its tips was never to run away. I had noticed that the annoying neighbour was smaller than me.

'Paki, Paki, Paki, go home! Paki, Paki, Paki!'

'I'm not from Pakistan. I'm from India.'

'Paki!' He stuck his tongue out.

'I'll hit you if you don't shut up.'

'Paki!'

I hit him hard with my right fist, straight in the face. He looked back at me, stunned, began furiously rubbing the place below his eyes where my blow had landed, burst into tears and ran off. I never saw him again. This encounter and the one with Daniel's dad were isolated incidents as my classmates and neighbours were usually extremely friendly, never treating me as someone who didn't belong. Sadly, Samantha continued to avoid me, but there was no way I would embrace a bland garlic-free diet; even for her.

I worried that a complaint would be made about my attack and during break next day mentioned the boy's repeated abuse to Mr Fisher, who had suffered at the hands of the Japanese during the Second World War. Sometimes he told us tales of starvation rations as a young prisoner of war and about horrific mistreatment and beatings. He suffered recurring bouts of malaria which made him tremble and clutch his head, as if dancing razor blades were attacking him inside. Over the next hour he would appear to recover until the shaking resumed, overwhelming him. At this stage he suddenly lost his temper and hurled the wooden blackboard rubber at anyone misbehaving, occasionally drawing blood, before disappearing for a few days. My experience with Shastriji had taught me to stay on the right side of teachers and I was never a victim. I always felt safe with Mr Fisher, which was more than could be said of my classmates.

'You mustn't worry about these boys, Bharat.' By now he aspirated the 'b' splendidly whenever he addressed me. 'They are fools; idiots who know no better. Let me tell you a story about Bradford's family. They came from Jamaica to find work here and in so many ways they are just like us. They speak English, they are Christian, they go to church every Sunday and they eat potatoes and meat. But people are always afraid of difference and they *lash out*, which means they are angry. They lash out because they are ignorant; in fact, we say pig-ignorant, which means they don't know any better.' Whenever new words cropped up I must have looked nonplussed, as if a giant question mark had appeared on my face. Mr Fisher could never resist the temptation to widen my vocabulary.

'Bradford's elder brothers were the first black boys at this school. I'd just started working here when they came and children asked to touch their faces to see whether they had painted the black on, or whether it was really their skin colour. It took them a while to understand that they were children, just like them. As you see, Bradford is a very popular boy who joins in with everything and has lots of friends. Outside school people sometimes call him names, but being intelligent he has learned to ignore them. Wasn't it your great leader, Gandhi, who never fought violence with violence and isn't that how he won his great victory? That's the way forward. You must simply walk away if provoked… 'Provoked' is when somebody tries to make you angry.' The question mark must have reappeared. 'If you have any problems you come and see me. Alright?'

I nodded and wandered home, reassured; but I was not convinced that *Gandhiji* would have had much joy practising *ahimsa* against my aggressor. I remembered the flying blackboard rubber. Mr Fisher, I decided, did not practise *ahimsa* himself. I had now researched Robert the Bruce and Braveheart in encyclopaedias and was familiar with their robust methods of dealing with enemies. I was also certain that neither Captain Marvel nor *Hanuman* would retreat from a fight. As I walked along I formulated my conclusions aloud, using the words I had just learned: 'I shall try hard not to lash out against my enemy because he is pig-ignorant, but if he lashes first I shall lash him harder. Much harder.' I hoped the first part of my strategy would please Gandhiji and knew that my friends, Robert, the Captain and *Hanuman*, would back me up on the second.

On my way back I noticed that a few people had put up trees and Christmas lights, but the festival meant nothing to us and we did not celebrate it. *Nani* was peering out of the door and as soon as she spotted me ran up to tell me that *Ba* and *Bapuji* were coming to England very soon. I was thrilled, anticipating our happy reunion: a return to the halcyon days when we all lived together in Africa.

We drove down to Heathrow to pick them up and about an hour after the plane landed I caught my first glimpse of *Bapuji* in almost three years and of *Ba* and Kumud in more than four. My sister had grown considerably. She was clinging on to my parents' arms and for once she was not crying. My brother Ramesh, however, was wailing merrily even though he was comfortably ensconced in *Bapuji*'s arms. *Nana's* son from his first marriage, Dinesh, was with them too. We were beginning to give each other nicknames at school and I decided to call my cousin 'Bacon', after the pig-producing country his name suggested. Mr Fisher, I recalled, had told us that Denmark is 'big on pigs'. As Dinesh spoke no English I had to wait months to reveal his new moniker.

On the way home I sensed something was wrong. My parents were delighted to see me; Dinesh, Ramesh and Kumud less so, though in fairness they were exhausted. It was a chilly day, the temperature had already hit its four degree high and was now plummeting. The new arrivals were all trembling. Their teeth made a clicking percussion as we climbed into the van. *Ba* held me close and asked a lot of questions about England, but whenever *Bapuji* spoke she glared at him. We stayed with Gangama until we could move into our rented house and for a few days all was reasonably civil.

The new house was an end terrace, full of cracks, mould and damp; but at last I had a bedroom of my own. Poor Kumud was forced to share with the noisy and boisterous Ramesh and I had to contend with something louder: my wallpaper. It screamed at me, begging to be torn off in strips: a dirty beige with yellow, purple and orange triangles and a cobweb adornment. A plant was growing into my room through the exposed outside wall and although the window was shut, a chill wind blew though. My winter would be challenging.

About nine o'clock that evening, after Kumud and Ramesh had gone to bed and I was closing the bathroom door, I heard raised voices. My parents rarely argued, so what followed was so compelling that I sat on the stairs to listen as the drama unfolded below.

'You never told me it would be this cold.'

'It's winter. It'll be warm soon.'

'Kusum told me it doesn't get warm for another six months and even then it is quite chilly.'

'You just have to wear some woollen sweaters. We'll buy them tomorrow.'

'This house is *really* cold. We can't live here. We would have to order a fire in every room every day. Now we have our own home I need at least two *doobras*.'

'You can't have *doobras*. Not here.'

A silence. *Ba's* voice was now shriller:

'What do you mean, I can't have *doobras*? Who will peel the vegetables? Who will sweep the floors and clean the house?'

'You will.'

'I will not. You must get *doobras*.'

'There are none. They're all in India. They are too poor to travel all this way.'

'Kusum said there are *doobras* who have come from Surat, in a place called 'Birmingham'. Go and get them.'

'No, no, they will not work for us. They are young, they've come to study at the university. They won't work for anyone.'

'In that case, tell Bhulima to send our *doobras*. You can wire the money for the tickets.'

'The British government will not allow that.'

Another silence.

'I don't mind having English servants. Or African ones, like we had in Nzuka.'

'Look, this government doesn't allow servants. It's different here. Everyone is equal. Servants are against the law.'

'Then I'm going home tomorrow. We're all going, so book the tickets. We left a big house, with *doobras*, in India to move to a smaller one in Africa and now look where you've brought us: to this godforsaken freezing hellhole where everybody is wrapped up and miserable! I'm not staying!'

So it continued until they ran out of arguments and *Ba* wept copiously, struggling for lungfuls of air as her misery overcame her. I empathised. I too had arrived expecting a better life and ended up in a cot. Now I quite liked it here. She just needed time to adjust.

# Chapter 17
## Survival

A piercing scream woke us next morning. We ran down to the kitchen to find *Ba* standing on a chair, trembling with fear. She was clutching her sari and hopping from foot to foot.

'Rats! This house is infested with rats!'

A squeak alerted us to a scurrying creature in the corner. It ran the length of the skirting board and vanished magically into a tiny hole even smaller than itself.

'It's only a mouse,' *Bapuji* said.

'I don't care what it is! I only know there are dozens of them and I want them out of the house. Now!'

What upset *Ba* most was that she had set up her mini *mandir* in the kitchen so she could perform *puja* after bathing. To furnish her new home with good fortune she had laid out coconut as an offering to *Ganesh* and it had been mercilessly nibbled away until little was left. Two small pieces lay on the floor, each resembling a map of Australia. Her *diwas* remained unlit and without the blessing of the gods the house was unsafe.

*Bapuji* had a plan, involving poison and cheese. He took me with him and we traipsed around half a dozen shops before unearthing the cheapest cheese and an expensive substance. It came in the shape of tiny sapphire grains which we were warned not to touch with our bare hands. *Bapuji* explained that the garish colour was to prevent us mixing up the poison with our *thali*.

*Ba* carefully grated some cheese, added a few blue granules and wrapped the concoction inside some *chappatis*. These she placed in strategic locations: in corners, by gaps in the skirting boards and outside the door. All day we heard scrabbling and scraping, but we didn't see one mouse. *Ba* refused to enter the kitchen alone and insisted one of us stayed with her while she cooked. She wore an expression combining rancour, revulsion and sheer terror and the lack of *doobras* to chop the vegetables intensified her temper.

The following day we found five mice lying peacefully on their sides. *Bapuji* had left early for a job interview and none of us were willing to remove the creatures from the kitchen. A knock on the door provided the answer, at a cost. *Foy* and *Fouaji* were both working in factories and *Ba* had agreed to look after our cousins, Anil and Mahendra. They were standing at the door as *Fouaji* drove away, tyres screeching.

They traipsed in and stared at the bodies. Anil looked disgusted and a little frightened but Mahendra immediately knelt down and picked one up. He told us he was already in charge of disposing of *Foy's* deceased mice. He was more than happy to bag them up and put them in the bin, as long as *Ba* was prepared to pay his usual fee: ten pence per carcase. The transaction was quickly completed and over the next few weeks Mahendra became the richest boy in the whole of Highfields.

*Ba* gamely tried to settle into her brave new world, but she needed inspiration. *Bapuji* began working long hours in a hosiery factory and when he came home he was always tired or busy. Because he could read and write English, friends and relatives arrived from all around, sometimes from as far as Birmingham and Derby, asking him to check and fill in a variety of documents, from job applications to driving licences and insurance forms. *Ba* turned to a frequent visitor, Ramanfouaji, *Fouaji's* brother. He was a jolly smiley man who always greeted us by holding out both hands, palms upturned. He expected us to slap them down, at which point he would shout, '*Shabash*!'

He was ever ready to join our football game or any game we happened to be playing. He adored winning and, despite his rotundity, could skip nimbly past us and slot the ball into the net, celebrating wildly in the manner of his hero, Eusebio. According to Ramanfouaji, Eusebio was the greatest player the world has ever seen *and* he played for Benfica, the finest and biggest club in the universe. Ramanfouaji supported the Lisbon team because he and *Fouaji* had taken a different route here from India: via the Portuguese colony, Mozambique. He spoke the language and used words we found confusing, like '*falta*' for foul and '*campo*' for pitch. '*Gol*', of course, we knew, but he had a way of bellowing it with a reverberating final letter. As he wheeled away in celebration you could hear his 'Golllllllllllllllllll!' through all the streets beyond.

'How do the English survive these awful winters?' *Ba* asked him after a game, huddling into her lacy cardigan.

'They eat meat and eggs and they drink Guinness.'

'I'm not touching meat or eggs. What is Guinness?'

'It's a drink they have. It's like a tonic, full of goodness. They say if you drink Guinness you don't need to eat or drink anything else. It's a sort of black milk, but better suited to their climate.'

'Very well. Get me some and I'll try it.'

Indians rarely buy anything from a shop if they can find a wholesaler; but that necessitates buying in bulk. *Bapuji* was already a member of Pankaj Cash and Carry and would bring home boxes of twenty-four packets of cheese and onion or salt and vinegar crisps in the belief that he was saving money. We found his hidden store and demolished his snacks almost as fast as he could buy them. It was also a gross financial error to purchase crates of Lucozade and Coca Cola.

Two days later Ramanfouaji returned with twenty-four bottles of Guinness and we all gathered round to watch *Ba* enjoy her first alcoholic drink. She had no idea that Guinness was not quite so full of goodness as Ramanfouaji and the adverts claimed. Ramanfouaji slowly poured the black nectar into a slanted glass until there was a lovely cream head on top. He handed it over to *Ba,* who examined it suspiciously.

'What do I do with this?'

'You drink it. It's quite bitter, like *karvat.*'

*Karvat* was our cure-all, an unpleasant mixture of herbs to relieve everything from indigestion to headaches. Most of my ailments had succumbed to *karvat* and, apart from my tonsil surgery and the accident on the ship, I had not troubled doctors. If an illness was prolonged *Ba* resorted to *bathhas* and constant prayer, all the while experimenting with a range of *ayurvedic* medicines involving extracts from around five thousand herbs. I had read that some are highly dangerous and should be banned, but their three-thousand-year history persuades millions the risk is worth taking.

Reassured by the mention of *karvat, Ba* picked up the glass, sniffed the contents, threw back her head and downed the Guinness in one go. The look on her face suggested it was an abominable experience. She puckered her lips and smacked them with her tongue, like a snake, and we assumed she was preparing to vomit. Instead, she leant forward and sat open-mouthed. What emerged was a Bhulima-style burp which resounded around the room, emitting a malty tang unlike anything we had ever encountered. Then, in a sudden reverse, the alcohol rush made her giddy and giggly and she began laughing uncontrollably.

'It's *vile*. Truly *horrible*... And you say they drink this every day?

'Every day.'

For the next twenty-three days *Ba* drank a bottle every evening and when the crate was empty she never touched a drop of Guinness again. She demanded new remedies to combat the persistent bitter weather. A brief snow flurry was greeted with ecstasy by her children; for her it was a foreboding of even grimmer days in store. She always dressed in a flimsy silk sari, which meant the lower part of her body was open to the glacial gusts from Siberia which were raging across the land. A pair of cotton socks, sandals and a thin nylon cardigan completed her outfit; I was convinced she would not survive the winter. As an experienced inhabitant, I now wore two pairs of socks, a vest and two jumpers.

Poor *Ba* was just beginning her acclimatisation and post–Guinness spent much of the time warming her hands in front of the coal fire or above the gas hob in the kitchen. It was pitiful. I vividly remembered my own introduction to the dismal days greeting my arrival. The cold water, the abrasive toilet paper, the missing sunshine, the dark, crowded dimly-lit rooms: all these memories came rushing back. Yet I was happy now and even enjoyed the changing seasons, though I couldn't have explained why. I hoped the same mysterious transformation would soon overcome *Ba*. For now, she believed that a happier hedonistic lifestyle lay five thousand miles away to the south or the east.

Over the next few weeks I sensed she had resigned herself to her fate. Her anger abated as she gradually realised there was no alternative *Bapuji* would accept. I had read an article in *Reader's Digest* with the headline, The Grass is always Greener and other Metaphors Explained. It related the tale of two neighbours who mistakenly envied each other as they looked over the fence, but after chatting realised they were happier just as they were. I realised they weren't only talking about their lawns and the meaning of this metaphor became clearer. Ironically, the grass *was* greener in England, because it rained so much all year round; but *Ba* had been sold a dream of Albion. No one had mentioned any downsides.

Eventually, in April, the days grew milder and there was a week of almost continual sunshine. Still *Ba* was never seen without her cardigan and her newly-acquired scarf and to save herself from perishing from the cold she had learned about stockings. As these shielded her nether regions a smile slowly returned to her face.

Ramanfouaji decided she still needed cheering up. Knowing that Chowpatty Beach was one of her favourite places, he arrived one day in a dilapidated red van and drove us all to Skegness. *Ba, Foy*, Kumud, Ramesh, Anil, Mahendra and I squeezed into a space designed for four adults. The van was fitted with seatbelts, but the only one in use was the one next to Kumud. She chewed it with relish until Ba noticed and told her to stop.

Ramanfouaji meant well, but he hadn't checked the forecast and a mighty gale was blowing across the flatlands of Lincolnshire, scattering leaves and gathering soil and dust into swirls, like a typhoon. I stared out of the window hoping to see large creatures rampaging across the countryside, but the view was sadly different to those I relished in India and Africa. True, there were cows and horses, but there the thrill ended. It was the dullest landscape I had ever seen: rows of low-lying fields bordered by occasional hedges, painted only in greens and browns. There was very little traffic: no rickshaws madly overtaking and honking horns; no sudden onrush of wild boars or camels.

We drove into a car park by the beach and covered our eyes as the sands arose angrily and flew through the air. The town claimed to be the happiest place on the east coast and posters of the Jolly Fisherman, his arms and legs akimbo, were everywhere. 'Skegness is so bracing!' he announced, and we had to agree with him. A dozen doleful bad-tempered donkeys were lined up at the entrance to the beach, waiting for passengers. Their *howdahs* were pathetic: just a mat slung across their backs, without any ornate coloured patterns or carvings. I had ridden on a camel on Chowpatty Beach and this lesser option didn't entice me. We all gazed at the view beyond them and *Ba* and I asked the same question simultaneously:

'Where is the sea?'

'Oh, it's there,' said Ramanfouaji. 'But you can't see it. It goes far out sometimes and then it comes back in. You will see it later.'

Gross disappointment and disillusionment flooded Ba's features. For a fleeting moment I imagined her face as a television screen, and on the screen I could see Chowpatty Beach. I could hear the hustle and bustle and my image was filled with elephants, camels, jugglers, *pau bhaji, garam chai* and *kulfi* sellers, snake charmers and performing monkeys. I could sense the vibrancy and joy thousands of miles away, smell the spices and the perfumes. In contrast, before me was the drab line of donkeys and a dozen hardy figures spread across a huge beach, all bowed down, not one looking remotely happy.

Ramanfouaji produced a football from his bag and we set up a makeshift goal and began playing, determined to enjoy ourselves. Poor *Ba* sat huddled on the sand, clutching her clothes tightly together and turning her head away from the sandstorm to avoid damaging her eyes. Ramanfouaji scored several goals, his grin growing wider with each moment of brilliance as he flung his arms into the air and ran off shouting in Portuguese. There were odd glances from people passing, but he was unconcerned. It was impossible to play football on Chowpatty Beach, he said, as it was so crowded. Here we had acres of space!

After an hour or so we retired to a fish and chip shop where *Ba* turned up her nose and sniffed disapprovingly as the fishy aroma hit her. We all ordered only chips, except for Ramanfouaji, who made no secret of his meat addiction. He had a huge appetite and his portion came accompanied by a fish and two giant sausages. I had not yet come out as a carnivore and looked longingly at the delicious fare on Ramanfouji's plastic plate.

By now the sea had come in, but the wind was blowing harder and the flying sands were more hazardous by the minute. As the charcoal clouds began unloading a steady drizzle we decided we had enjoyed enough of bracing Skegness and began the long journey home through the monotonous Lincolnshire fields. As there was not a hill in sight I could see for miles, yet there were no delights or quirks to admire. I looked around the van. Everyone but Ramanfouaji was asleep.

# Chapter 18

## England, our England

The *Reader's Digest* published an article about loneliness and how to avoid it. I had the solution: marry a Patel. In a Patel household droves of visitors arrive uninvited all day and every day. Now that *Fouaji* had sold his shop, accepting that he was unable to source sufficient aubergine-eaters, the number of Asians in Highfields had grown exponentially. Most hailed from Munsari or Surat and neighbouring villages. This resulted in complex interconnections, making us all related, no matter how distantly. Someone's brother-in-law's cousin's son had married someone from your own family, so that linked you to another hundred people. *Ba* knew every twig of this overgrown family tree, but the relationships were a mystery to me and I glazed over whenever they were explained.

If people were unrelated in any other way, the fact that they came from a neighbouring village at once made them your kin. *Ba* managed to befriend at least fifty women who trooped in one after another and sometimes three or four at once. She really could have done with a servant or two to tackle the chores while she was in full-time employment exchanging news and gossip. This band of women shopped together, had *masala* tea and *bhajias* together, they organised *poppadum* parties and went en masse to see Bollywood movies. They even went on a short *jatra* to a new *mandir* in London on a hired coach. Somehow the spiritual encounter resulted in a clutch of expensive new outfits which returned with them in bags labelled *'Sari Mandir'*. *Ba* was finally settling down and enjoying her new life.

Most visitors came only for an hour or two, but quite often whole families stayed overnight, which meant I had to give up my room and sleep downstairs on the living room sofa. I was introduced to everyone and reminded of our mutual connections and I nodded away, trying to look interested: an exercise guaranteed to produce a foolish expression. In reality I was furious because I would again lose my precious room and my privacy. Furthermore, I would be woken at some ungodly hour as the gods had to be appeased at dawn every day in the room where I was sleeping. The light would be turned on, making further sleep impossible, and a noisy *puja* would ensue, topped off with the ringing of a bell and some tuneless singing. Because the ritual is scheduled for dawn Hindus tend to go to bed early, tumbling downstairs bleary-eyed to perform their religious duty.

One evening, after my parents and guests had retired at nine-thirty, I made a secret plan to watch television until late. Nobody would know as long as I kept the sound down and if someone came down unexpectedly the noisy creaking of the fourth and ninth stairs would alert me. I had a book ready under my pillow so that it would be assumed I was reading. No Patel child would be scolded for reading late as it shows such laudable devotion to study.

I would have enjoyed a book more that night as I made the mistake of watching Alfred Hitchcock's *Psycho*, which left me horror-struck. By the early hours I was lost in nightmares, so I was delighted to be awoken by a knock on the window. I had been dreaming that a man with a dagger was chasing me to the screeching violin accompaniment of a film I was too young to watch. I was running away, screaming and trying to keep him at bay by hurling *chappatis*. I glanced at my watch. It was two o'clock.

Through the curtains hovered the grim and fearful face of Manojkaka, lit by the flickering street lamp. His body was hidden by the darkness. He had sharp features, a huge bandit moustache and out-of-control eyebrows and his expression resembled my own three hours previously when Norman Bates was butchering Marion Crane in the shower. Clearly something had horrified him, too.

Manojkaka was a friend of *Bapuji's* who owned a bar and restaurant named the Tip-Top Gentleman's Private Club. It had a scruffy and forbidding entrance and blacked-out windows. The door was plastered with strict red and yellow notices warning Admittance Solely for Members, Sorry, Cash Only and Reputable Establishment, Please Behave! I hadn't been allowed inside but Ashok, a friend of mine who had, told me the walls were black and covered with life-size colour posters of scantily-dressed women. The menu was restricted to meat dishes. Ashok's Dad ate there often as his wife refused to cook meat and he had allowed his son to try a chicken *biryiani,* which was absolutely delicious.

I knew that you could get alcohol well beyond licensing hours because I had heard *Bapuji* asking Manojkaka how he got away with it. He said it was not a problem because all the police drank there as they had complimentary membership. He came occasionally to share a Bacardi and Coke with *Bapuji* and they played cards and chess together. They knew each other from their days in Zambia, though I had no memory of him. His wife, Dakshakaki, was an intimidating woman who was forever scolding him for small offences. She would yell at him to wipe his moustache if she detected the merest crumb. She chided him like a child and he was terrified of her. It was not difficult for a former member of the Terrible Three to deduce that working long and late hours was an immense relief to Manojkaka, enabling him to escape his persecutor.

I opened the door and saw a yellow taxi behind him with the engine still running. Although it was springtime an icy blast blew in, so I beckoned him inside and shut the door. It was then that I noticed he wore no trousers. His voluminous underpants flapped under shirt-tails which were torn and covered in mud, but he had kept his socks and shoes on. His teeth chattered and he was skipping from one foot to the other as goosebumps popped out on his thighs.

'Go, get *Bapuji*; go now, quickly. Go, go!'

I dutifully trotted upstairs, shook *Bapuji* awake and he came down grumpily and speedily when I whispered Manojkaka's name in his ear.

'What's happened? Where are your trousers?'

'Never mind my trousers. Can you lend me a pound for the taxi fare?'

*Bapuji* handed Manojkaka the money and he dashed out of the door and back within thirty seconds. His goosebumps had multiplied and he was shaking uncontrollably.

'So, what happened?'

It was a long story.

'I left the club at midnight and walked home as usual. I popped into the casino, as I do from time to time, and I had a good night. I mean a really good night, best ever: won over two hundred pounds, which I put in my back trouser pocket. A fat bloke I'd seen there before followed me out and as I turned the corner he rushed at me and knocked me to the pavement. I was a bit stunned and he must have seen me put the money away because he tried to get his hands inside my trouser pocket, but it was too tight. So he pushed me down, ripped my trousers off and ran away and before I could get up he'd disappeared down a side street. I've never seen anyone that fat move so fast! Anyway, I went to the police station to report it and they ordered me a taxi.'

'Why didn't you go home?'

'I'd have had to wake Daksha and ask her for the taxi money. She sleeps with the money under her pillow and she would have killed me. Can I borrow a pair of trousers? If she wakes up and sees me like this I'm in big trouble.'

*Bapuji* went back upstairs and returned with a trouser selection. Manojkaka chose a pair and slunk off into the night, but before we had shut the door he turned round and strode back. He glared at me.

'Not a word to Dakshakaki. Okay?'

'Okay.'

Two months later, relegated again to the broken-spring sofa, I was wakened by more desperate banging and thumping. This time I found Hasmukhkaka and Lilakaki and their two toddlers on the doorstep with all their worldly goods in six suitcases. We were not related, but as they were from Ganeshgam they were almost family. A month ago we had said our goodbyes when they sold their shop and flew to Zambia. *Bapuji* had advised against it because there was unrest in Lusaka, the capital, caused by the declining economy and strict government controls. A relative of ours who ran a garage in Nzuka had been held up at gunpoint and shot dead after refusing to hand over the money. But Hasmukhkaka insisted on emigrating: he wanted to return to a land filled with sunshine, open spaces and opportunity. Even *Ba* tried to dissuade him, but he was adamant.

'Go, go! Get *Bapuji* and *Ba*.'

Half an hour later *Ba* was frying *bhajias* and making tea as we listened to the dismal tale of the returned emigrants. They had loved the house in Nzuka and for the first three weeks the weather had been glorious; but occasionally they heard sounds of fighting and once of gunfire. Then three days ago gunshot shattered their living room window and they were sprayed with glass. Luckily the police were outside and arrests were made, but Hasmukhkaka decided it was too risky to stay with a young family. As usual our house was the refuge of choice, not only for visiting relatives but for trouserless men and fleeing families. That night four more residents moved in until they could find accommodation. I despaired of ever getting my room back.

The gun warfare in Nzuka finally persuaded *Ba* that Leicester was not just a safe place, it was now her home. *Mandirs* and Bollywood cinemas had sprung up and so had shops selling wider selections of Indian groceries. Best of all, there was now a *sari* and jewellery emporium. She had lately developed hypochondria, a condition requiring a visit to Dr Drake every few days for the most minor ailments, from a sniffle to a sudden pain in a leg or an ear. Ayurvedic medicines were abandoned in favour of the new science and she was never happier than when arriving home with a cache of multi-coloured pills. Miraculously, her pains often vanished before she took a single one and she dutifully returned her unused medicines.

The summer came and retreated, leaving all of us more cheerful for the warmth and sunshine. During these months *Ba* did not visit the doctor as often and passers-by observed her on the doorstep chopping chillis, garlic and coriander, soaking up the sun like a reptile, gathering strength and energy. We boys were out all day long playing football, cricket and tennis and afterwards enjoying an orange or strawberry Jubbly: a huge pyramid of ice soaked in fruit juice which could be sucked with great but diminishing pleasure as we extracted the juice, and made to last a full hour.

Suddenly it was time to begin the high-level education prophesied in my *janmotri.* At primary school, with one or two exceptions, we dressed like waifs and strays from a Dickens' novel, but now I had to wear a smart uniform so that we would all appear to be of equal status. That was the theory. In practice, cheaper school uniforms were available at the Co-op on High Street while expensive, tailored outfits were purveyed by Knight's, of Granby Street. We took one look at the price tickets in Knight's window and scurried back to the Co-op.

I had acquired a vast knowledge of English surnames. I knew that Adamson was merely the son of an Adam in the distant past; that Barkers were once leather tanners, their name relating to the Old English verb 'to tan' and not to doggy noises and that though Cooper may have made barrels long ago he could now be anything from a bin man to a brain surgeon. Nonetheless, unexpected names still captivated me and made me smile. At the first register the alphabet began with common names: Atkinson, Anderson, Barber and Bell; but every now and then a surname compelled me to make a note, so I could research its provenance.

'Death.'

'Sir.'

'Dick.'

'Sir.'

'Nutter.'

'Sir.'

'Willey.'

I had definitely entered the right class. No other could offer such bizarre riches, such joy, to a student of the English language.

After assembly our form teacher, Mr Stott, told us that he had been a vicar until the Lord suggested his true calling was to hammer knowledge into the thick skulls he could see before him. He was high on heavy-handed humour, low on wit. It was difficult to imagine him as a man of the cloth as he rounded on any boy talking when he should have been listening and clouted him viciously on the head. Donald Tryke became the butt of his fondness for violence. One afternoon, when Tryke continued chattering, he was ordered to go to the library and return with the large dictionary, which he laid on Mr Stott's desk. Mr Stott stood up, picked up the weighty tome and thumped him on the head with it. Tryke looked baffled, tottered and shook his head, stupefied. He stared up at his assailant.

'Now take it back.'

When Tryke chewed gum he was invited to spit it onto Mr Stott's outstretched palm. The gum was then rubbed into the hair at the back of his head and next day Tryke returned with a clump missing, revealing what was almost, but not quite, a bald patch. My cowardice helped me stay out of trouble, but Tryke was not to be tamed and provided regular entertainment as he suffered at the hands of the lapsed vicar. He and Mr Stott maintained a war of attrition; they made a fine art of effortlessly provoking one another. Happily for Tryke, our other teachers were less demented and he was less inclined to take liberties with them, attracting only detentions. Struck by the contrasting behaviour of my form teacher and his colleagues, I wondered whether Mr Stott had been in the same prisoner of war camp as Mr Fisher. It was the most likely explanation. It was barely credible that the Lord had sent him unto Tryke to unleash his latent brutality.

Our music teacher, Mr Constable, scored as highly as Mr Stott on my oddity scale. He wore a different polka-dotted bow tie every day with an unvarying pink shirt and he held his head erect, like a peacock. The iridescent blue scarf he occasionally sported perfected his plumage. He strutted about, bobbing and inclining his head like a courting bird even when playing the piano, pausing only to pop a purple pill into his mouth. The rumour was that he took 'pep pills'. On playground duty he hummed loudly to relieve the ennui and ordered nearby boys to join in the tune. If they refused he put them in detention.

My *janmotri* had decreed a sparkling musical future. Unlike many of my classmates, I had never had private lessons or owned an instrument. Three of them owned pianos, well beyond our means. I had, however, been chosen to sing in the Leicestershire Junior Choir at Leicester's De Montfort Hall. Indeed, everyone in our class had been chosen, as were several other classes from schools throughout the county. When Mr Constable asked if anyone had sung in a choir I put up my hand along with eight other boys.

He lined us up against the wall and began playing *Waltzing Matilda* on his piano. We had the words on a printed sheet and he asked each boy to sing a verse in turn; but when I sang he turned from the keys with a loud discord and a glare of pain and consternation. I thought he needed a pep pill. Instead he stalked over and scowled down venomously at me from above his jaunty violet bow.

'You: *out*! Go and sit in the hall until the lesson is over. I've never heard such caterwauling in all my life.'

My musical career had ended before it began. Stunned and outraged, I wondered how many more of the soothsayer's forecasts would prove to be false.

At home there was more money around as the textile market was competitive and the wages decent for qualified knitters like *Bapuji*. We were never short of food or clothing, though we didn't spend money on anything unnecessary; like haircuts, for example. On Saturday afternoons an itinerant barber knocked on the door and set up in front of the television during the wrestling. For the cost of a single visit to Sunil's Smart Snipz Salon, Bapuji could have the whole family shorn. The results were unlike the glossy styles modelled by Bollywood stars in Sunil's window and occasionally our heads looked lopsided; but we were unfazed. Bikhukaka specialised in short back and sides and he was unable to produce anything else, no matter how thick and lustrous your hair.

*Fouaji* refused to employ Bikhukaka, having once suffered an unkind cut which left him looking like Gandhiji. He could afford Smart Snipz now that he was working for an engineering firm, his expensive blip with the aubergines behind him. He always thought big and when the opportunity arose he set up a restaurant at the edge of the city centre. It had an eclectic menu which included moussaka, *biriyani*, kebabs, chow mein, paella, coq au vin and chicken and chips. He refused to serve beef.

*Fouaji* would stand on the doorstep in an apron urging customers to 'Eat Round the World Here!' Friends and relations were allowed in free. He had many friends and relations. Parked outside was a Rolls Royce with an Indian flag on the bonnet, fluttering gaily in the breeze. When he took Mahendra and me for a spin he proclaimed that he must be the only Indian in the whole country driving the king of cars and the car of kings.

It was an old Phantom V, capable of more than a hundred miles an hour:

sleek and with appropriate aubergine paintwork. The plush leather seats were a steep upgrade on our second-hand moth-eaten sofas. Its engine was so smooth you couldn't tell that it was running: when I excitedly asked *Fouaji* to start the motor he turned round, grinning, and said it was already on. Mahendra and I sat in the back and waved like the Queen at gawping passers-by, most of whom had only seen a Rolls Royce on *Pathé* news. Indians riding in the world's premier car must have been as unlikely as airborne pigs. *Fouaji* drove us to his house which was on a narrow street where parking was straightforward as the Rolls was the only car there. Everyone else went by bus.

A fortnight later a dirty white van was parked in its place. It had seen better days, with bumps and bruises all along the body and signs of rust. *Fouaji* was climbing out of it, as cheerful as ever. You rarely saw him without a grin, even in times of adversity.

'*Fouaji*, what happened to the Roller?'

'Eight miles to the gallon, that's what happened. The scoundrels who sold it me never said it was that hungry. I went to Coventry last week and it bankrupted me! But *Rama* always looks after you: this van is more practical for carrying onions and drums of cooking oil. Come in and I'll rustle you up a delicious new dish I've invented. You fry onions, peppers, tomatoes, chillis and throw in a few spices and fresh coriander, add diced potatoes and a few eggs and you've got everything you need, all done in twenty minutes!'

It was not long before the restaurant went the same way as the Phantom and the aubergines. *Fouaji*'s excellent cooking didn't compensate for his largesse, which guaranteed any acquaintance a stupendous complimentary meal and drinks besides. His accountant told him the sums did not add up and *Fouaji* returned to engineering, unembittered. How many Indians had set up businesses in Mozambique and Portugal, owned a shop in England, a Rolls Royce and a restaurant by the time they were thirty-five?

Ramanfouaji too was thriving and had opened his own club and restaurant. One weekend he turned up with a dozen eggs, but he failed to subvert *Ba*'s vegetarianism.

'But this isn't meat. You drink milk from a cow, so why not eat eggs from a hen?'

'That's different. I will not eat eggs. You can cook them for everyone else because they'll need English food to survive when the weather gets worse again.'

Ramanfouaji prepared an enormous chilli and tomato omelette. We accompanied it with ketchup instead of lime pickle as we were slowly becoming anglicised.

We were beginning our slow descent into meat acceptance. Once a month the aroma of a chicken, potato and tomato curry filled the house and you would usually find *Fouaji* or Ramanfouaji stirring it. *Ba* learned to make meat dishes, keeping a look of revulsion and disdain on her face for as long as they were on the stove, but she refused point blank to taste them. Despite this, her creations tasted even better than those of the master chefs who taught her. We so admired her culinary powers that they became a rod for her own back: whenever we were invited to eat at a relative's house we refused to go unless she promised to cook there and the poor woman never rested.

Our diet remained mainly vegetarian, though occasionally we splashed out and returned home laden with packets of chips and sausages. *Bapuji* rarely touched meat: he would lay his chips flat on a plate, cover them with chilli powder until they were entirely red and eat them with a lemon squeezed over the top. Like *Bhulima*, he covered lemon quarters with salt and chilli powder and ate them whole, peel included; although he did make the concession of spitting out the pips. He had never read *Debrett's* because instead of removing them unobtrusively from his mouth he would shoot them out and catch them eighteen inches away, like a performing monkey. Irritatingly, he had inherited *Bhulima's* belch, which he trumpeted even more loudly and ostentatiously.

Now that we were carnivores *Fouaji* persuaded *Bapuji* that religious festivals and holidays were times of celebration and should include abundant meat. After all, Christmas dinner seemed to be almost entirely about a giant turkey. Without the turkey it was just another meal.

Until now we had ignored Yuletide. Even *Diwali* was a damp squib. All we had was a pathetically small box of fireworks, including at least one banger or rocket which would not light, and sparklers which seemed tired and flickered reluctantly and intermittently. I suspected they had been lying around for years unsold in Pankaj's Cash and Carry, because it was famous for never knowingly throwing old stock away. Besides, we had lost the joy of fireworks since Anil set a spare room alight the previous year, causing massive damage and the threat of a family-wide ban. *Fouaji* was furious, but *Foy* calmed him down and Anil was forgiven in time for the next *Diwali*.

I recalled past *Diwalis* in Ganeshgam and Nzuka when every house had a twinkling *diwa* on its doorstep, which created an enchanting glow as dusk fell. Then the fireworks would pop, snap, crackle and sparkle here, there and everywhere and continue until well past midnight. Joyful faces were illuminated by the *diwas*, just like on a Christmas card, as friends and relatives visited each other and exchanged gifts. These were not elaborate, usually involving little more than a few *pendas, barfi or laddoos.* That spirit and sense of occasion had died now we lived in England. It seemed that Indian families were too weary to rejoice, worn down by the burden of making ends meet and coping with the new, harsher climate.

At school when my friends asked what I would be getting for Christmas I chanted my list, which included a bike, a Polaroid camera and Scalextric. They became instantly and immensely jealous as they were expecting far less, not realising that I would get nothing at all. That was about to change. This Christmas, *Fouaji* decreed, there would be presents all round and meat to follow, and I awoke full of anticipation. He had experimented with turkey curries, but there was something fundamentally wrong about them and he altered his plans. Our Hindu Christmas would be constructed around chicken and lamb. By seven o'clock in the morning my nostrils were full of cumin, cloves, turmeric, garlic, ginger and chilli. I dashed downstairs to find Fouaji making *biryiani.*

He was frying carrots, onions, peas and other vegetables, each separately, in ghee, adding spices and then setting them aside. He had marinated the chicken pieces overnight in yoghurt, cumin, garlic and herbs and they were now roasting in the oven. When everything was ready, *Fouaji* orchestrated a masterly symphony of all these ingredients. Meanwhile, *Ba* was producing minced lamb and chicken samosas. She had already fried four types of *poppadums,* broken them up into a giant bowl and made a *raita.* In the corner was a vegetarian corn, carrot and green bean *biryiani*, just for her. On a shelf stood a bowl *of barfis, jalebis* and *laddoos.*

The presents, wrapped in newspaper, were now produced. I unwrapped a pound note and a scarlet nylon shirt. Kumud had a doll and some red ribbons and Ramesh a toy car and a dozen marbles. We were thrilled.

By now another five families had turned up and three groups formed in various rooms: men, women and children. The house was alive with the hubbub of people enjoying themselves as they played, squabbled and gossiped in raucous amicable Gujarati style. It had never been like this before. We were partying like the English! The unmistakeable voice of Lata Mangeskar lifted our spirits as the only LP we possessed spun on repeat and at last I could see why my classmates became ecstatic at the prospect of Christmas.

At midday all the men went off to the pub; they returned two hours later and opened a pack of Churchill cigars. Bapuji did not smoke, yet over the next two days he got through a dozen of them and drank more than his share of three bottles of Bacardi. For the rest of the year he would be a teetotal non-smoker again. This set the trend for Christmases to come. It was a time to 'become English', to live as the English lived; to cast aside all the primness and constraints of the Patels. As the rooms echoed with laughter I noticed *Ba* with a look of quiet contentment on her face. Her belly had swelled and we guessed that another baby was on the way, though no announcement had been made.

This unlovely place with its grimy streets and miserable weather, where no one had servants and you had to do the menial tasks yourself, you used nasty toilet paper and bathrooms were a luxury; where the sun rarely shone, rain threatened almost every day and in winter it was dark by half past three in the afternoon: this godforsaken place, as *Ba* had once described it, had imperceptibly become our home. This was our England, a place where we belonged. Finally, the search across three continents for greener grass had ended, ironically in a house with no garden, without a single blade.

# Afterword

*'Janmotri Bharatkumar Dahyabhai Patel, born in Ganeshgam, district Valsad.*

*'Bharat will be happy throughout his life and educated to the highest standard. However, he will be forced to travel far, far away to achieve this. He will visit many countries and see many things. When he is 21 he will leave education or else continue until he is 25 and after that he will earn lots of money and have a long and healthy life. He will have a special interest in music and play many instruments beautifully. He will be famous for his melodious singing. Wherever he goes, he will never be far from his family and he will look after his parents, his own children and even his relatives. He will marry at eighteen, or at twenty-five. He will choose his own partner and love her dearly and they will be most happy together and have at least two healthy and happy children. He will impart his great knowledge to his friends. He will have lots of cars and enjoy them tremendously. His karma says he will achieve the very best and will keep striving until he does so.'*

As I read my *janmotri,* carefully stored by *Ba* in an inlaid sandalwood box, I have to admit that some of the prophecies have come true. I remind myself that the same applies to newspaper horoscopes, because you can interpret them in any way you like. A friend who was a local newspaper trainee was asked to write the forecasts revealing every reader's future. When he protested that he knew nothing about astrology the editor told him to unearth ten-year-old horoscopes from the archives and use them verbatim. No one would notice, the editor said, and as no letters of complaint arrived it seems no one did.

But the truth is that my life would have been different, were it not for the soothsayer in Africa. His prediction of my excellent education, attained only by travelling afar, set events in train which led to us arriving in England when we did. We might have stayed in Zambia, or even returned to India. I will never know whether the soothsayer opened an invisible door which determined my fate, or whether all doors would have opened to the same prospect.

The education hailed as my destiny ended in a postgraduate course in journalism at the University of Cardiff where I met my wife, Andy. As the soothsayer prophesised, I did choose my own partner, which was rare for Hindus at the time; though she came without a factory.

The soothsayer was correct about the outcome of this meeting, though he failed to foresee the anguish Bhulima and my parents suffered when I rejected an arranged marriage. During that difficult time my sister Kumud acted as go-between and happily the rift was healed and the bonds strengthened when our children Natalie and Alex were born. Bhulima held them each in her lap and cried joyful tears.

However, he was in charlatan territory when he proclaimed my musical talents. Before any church service, or any event where there is singing, I am ordered to mouth the words silently. When I disobey Andy giggles uncontrollably and we have to leave.

I am puzzled by the reference to cars. I have owned nine but sadly have never known the rapture of Fouaji, who for two glorious weeks drove a Rolls Royce Phantom.

Aside from the *janmotri*, I must record that Bhulima, Gangama, Bapuji, Fouaji and Ramanfouaji are no longer with us; but Nani is still dancing. I can confirm that we all acclimatised to the British weather, some by following Ramanfouaji's prescription of Guinness and meat and others by sheer determination, interspersed by long winter stays in India. Ba is on a *jatra* in the Gujarat as I write. Having complained of the cold in sunless Leicester before she left she is now moaning about the heat in sunny Surat; so she has acquired at least one British trait. She is even looking forward to returning to the chill winds and rain of Leicester, which shows how much has changed since the grim day she landed at Heathrow.

# Glossary

**Aarti** – Hindu ritual in which the light of a **diwa** is offered to deities

**Achha** – okay, fine, alright

**Agarbatti** – joss stick

**Ahimsa** – respect for all living things, leading to non-violence

**Anant Lau** – uninterrupted light, a divine flame which burns for ever

**Ashram** – religious retreat, holy place or monastery

**Avatar** – manifestation of a deity or soul in bodily form on earth

**Ayurvedic** – Hindu system of medicine which decrees that mental health, stress and illness can all be treated by herbs and meditation

**Ba** – mum, mummy, mother

**Bapu** – father; also refers to Gandhi, father of the nation

**Bapuji** – dad, daddy, father

**Barfi** – dense milk sweet with cardamom

**Bataka** – potato

**Bathha** – a vow taken that if something comes about you will do penance in return

**Ben** – sister; when attached to a name it conveys respect or reverence, eg Bhuliben

**Benchod** – the most common Indian swear word, used in the same way as 'shit' or 'damn' in English, but can also be far cruder, referring to sex with one's sister

**Bhagwad Gita** – seven-hundred verse Sanskrit scripture which is part of the Hindu epic, **Mahabharata**

**Bhai** – brother; when attached to a name it conveys respect or reverence, eg   Bharatbhai

**Bhajia** – cakes or balls of spicy vegetables fried in batter

**Bhel puri** – traditional street food with puffed rice, vegetables, nuts, tamarind and fresh coriander

**Bidi** – hand-rolled cigarette

**Biryiani** – rice dish with vegetables to which you can add meat or fish, served dry or with a vegetable sauce or **raita**

**Brahmin** – the highest caste; the priest caste

**Chalo** – let's go, off you go, onward

**Champals** – sandals, usually like flip-flops but made of leather

**Chapatti** – flatbread, very thin in the Gujarat, slightly thicker in other parts of India

**Charpoy** – a wooden bed frame with interlaced cords or webbing, literally 'four legs'

**Chevro** – Bombay mix

**Dada** – grandfather or granddad or used to address anyone very old

**Dalit** – Sanskrit for 'broken' or 'scattered', the underclass who are said to be 'untouchable'

**Darshan** – viewing a holy person or an image of a deity, followed by prayer

**Desi daru** – lowest form of alcohol, usually made from grains or fruits

**Dhal** – thin lentil soup used as a dip or to accompany dishes like **masala dhosa,** vegetable curries and rice; a good source of protein

**Dhobi** – washerman or washerwoman

**Dhokla** –spicy snack made from fermented rice and chickpea flour

**Diwa** – lamp which burns using ghee or oil. The Hindu festival **Diwali,** the festival of lights, is named for it

**Diwali** – Hindu festival of lights, the biggest religious celebration of the year

**Doobra** – derogatory word for **Dalits,** who are also known as 'untouchables'.

**Fafra** – long rectangular fried crispy snack with carom seeds and black pepper, served with a variety of chutneys and fried chillis

**Faluda** – cold dessert or drink with vermicelli, rose syrup, cold milk and ice cream

**Farsan** – savoury snacks

**Fouaji** – uncle, your father's brother or brother-in-law

**Foy** – aunt, your father's sister or sister-in-law

**Galora** – a small green gourd sliced and mixed with onions, tamarind and spices to make a curry

**Gandhiji** – the father of the nation, **'ji'** added to his name to signify respect, who led India to independence in 1947

**Ganesh** – the elephant god, known for his wisdom and for bringing good fortune to his followers

**Garam chai** – hot tea

**Gathia** – crunchy snack in strands made from deep-fried chickpea flour

**Ghee** – clarified butter

**Gilli danda** – game similar to cricket but using a large stick to hit a smaller stick, pointed at both ends; runs are scored while it is retrieved

**Goatlee** – the mango stone, given to the youngest child to suck like a sweet until all the flesh comes off

**Gobi aloo** – cauliflower and potato curry

**Gorias** – derogatory term for white people

**Gram** – flour made from chickpeas

**Gunda** – thug, gangster, bully or criminal

**Hanuman** – the monkey god who can fly, lift mountains and grow to an enormous size and shrink to virtual invisibility

**Hathi** – elephant

**Hijab** – head covering worn by Muslim women

**Hindustan! Zindabad!** – Long live India! The most common battle cry before Partition

**Hing** – asafoetida, a pungent spice extracted from a plant of the fennel family, known for its digestive properties. Commonly called 'devil's dung'.

**Holi** – Hindu festival of colours, held in spring to mark the triumph of good over evil, in which people cover each other in brightly-coloured powders

**Howdah** – seat on an elephant's back, often ornate

**Idli** – rice cakes served with **dhal** and coconut chutney

**Jaisi Krishna!** – Hail, Lord **Krishna**!, a common greeting meaning 'hello'

**Jalebi** – deep-fried flour and sugar syrup, bright orange and shaped like a pretzel

**Janmotri** – horoscope

**Jatra** – pilgrimage which involves almsgiving

**Jaya he!** – Victory to thee! Part of the Indian national anthem

**Jaya gana mana** – Thou art the ruler of our minds, the Indian national anthem

**Ji** – added to a name it is a term of respect, eg **Gandhiji**

**Jibroo** – the act of sticking out the lower lip and curling it down when you are sad or sulky

**Kachori** – fried pastry balls containing spicy peas, crushed chickpeas or urad or moong dhal

**Kafni** – traditional billowing Indian trousers

**Kaka** – uncle, not only someone related but any older and wiser man

**Kaki** – aunt, not only someone related but any older and wiser woman

**Karela** – a bitter gourd which is curried and sweetened

**Karvat** – bitter herbal medicine said to cure all ailments

**Kem cho** – hello

**Khadi** – thin yoghurt and turmeric alternative to **dhal**, finished off with a **vagar. Re**sembles soup but served as a dip or to accompany rice

**Khitchya** – thick brown **poppadums** made from rice flour

**Kimam paan** – **paan** with tobacco; see also **paan**

**Kori** – coast

**Krishna** – the most widely-revered Hindu god; made cows holy because they provide milk, sustaining life

**Kufi** – prayer cap worn by Muslim men

**Kulfi** – dense creamy Indian ice cream, often flavoured with fruits and nuts like mango and pistachio

**Kumar** – prince, child or son; in address, a mark of respect, eg Rameshkumar

**Kurta** – upper garment

**Kwacha** – Zambian currency

**Laddoos** – spherical sweets made with milk, flour, nuts and raisins

**Lal** – darling or precious; a sign of respect when attached to a name, eg Chandulal

**Lassi** – cooling drink made with yoghurt, water and spices

**Lathi** – heavy wooden stick, often used by police for crowd control

**Laxmi – Vishnu's** wife

**Lengha** – trousers

**Lilva** – pigeon peas

**Ma** – grandma, granny, grandmother

**Mahabharata** – Hindu epic which details the struggle between two groups of cousins and is the primary source of the religion's ethics and history

**Maharajah** – ruler or king

**Maharani** – wife or widow of a **Maharajah**

**Mahout** – an elephant rider, trainer or keeper

**Mama** – uncle who is your mother's brother or brother-in-law

**Mami** – aunt who is your mother's sister or sister-in-law

**Mandap** – a tent with pillars erected for a wedding

**Mandir** –Hindu temple

**Mane orkhay**? – do you know who I am?

**Maru nam su che?** – what's my name, then?

**Masala** – a mixture of spices used in Indian cooking or tea

**Masala dhosa** – an ultra-thin rice paper pancake stuffed with potato curry and served with **dhal** and coconut chutney, a traditional meal in the south of India

**Methi** – fenugreek

**Mithu** – salt

**Motima** – elderly grandmother worthy of great respect; very senior figure

**Namaste** – 'Hello' or 'how are you?' Sanskrit greeting meaning 'I bow to the God within'

**Om namah Shivaya** – I bow to the Auspicious One

**Paan** – betel leaf filled with herbs, spices, nuts or fruits and good for digestion; can be made into a stimulant by adding tobacco and other drugs

**Paneer** – curd cheese

**Paratha** – flatbread, thicker than a chapatti

**Patidar** – a caste of Patels who were given strips of land to cultivate by the ruling classes

**Patra** – snack made of colocasia leaves spread with tamarind and chickpea flour, steamed and finished with sesame seeds and coconut

**Pau Bhaji** – thick vegetable curry served on soft bread, popular fast food

**Penda** – sugary snack made with milk and nuts

**Pijamo** – loose-fitting shirt

**Poori** – unleavened deep-fried bread which puffs up into an oval

**Poppadum** – large thin circular crisp made with flour, water and spices, an accompaniment to Indian meals; can be grilled or fried

**Puja** – Hindu prayer ritual

**Pukka** – genuine, the real deal; from the Hindi word meaning 'solid' or 'first class'

**Pungi** – wind instrument used by snake charmers

**Raita** – yoghurt dip containing onion or cucumber and spices

**Rama** – major Hindu deity who defeated the demon **Ravana** and returned to his kingdom in Ayodhya to be greeted by lit **diwas**. This is the origin of the Hindu festival of lights, **Diwali**

**Ramayana** – Hindu epic which tells of **Rama**'s struggle to rescue his wife **Sita** from the demon **Ravana**

**Ravana** – ten-headed demon king of Sri Lanka

**Rotla** – thick chapatti, similar to **paratha**

**Sadhu** – itinerant holy man who wanders from **ashram** to **ashram,** begging

**Sahib** – polite form of address to a man, eg Doctor Sahib

**Sai Baba** – saint revered by both Hindus and Muslims; his shrine in Shirdi is a popular pilgrim destination

**Samosa** – triangular deep-fried pastry filled with spicy vegetables

**Sari** – single piece of cotton or silk worn by women, draped around the body

**Saru che** – fine, thank you, or how are you?

**Shabash!** – Bravo! Well done!

**Shaak** – vegetable curry

**Shiva** – one of the three main Hindu deities, known as the Destroyer because he removes evil from the world

**Shrikhand** – sweet curd pudding with nuts

**Sita** – **Rama's** wife

**Sopari** – areca nut which is shaved and put into **paan**

**Swastika** – ancient symbol of divinity and spirituality, bastardised by the Nazis to represent their Aryan descent

**Tabla** – pair of small hand drums, one larger than the other

**Tamru** – a two-headed drum, used by **Shiva**

**Tandoor** – clay oven used in north India

**Tari Hiri** – a day of penance on which food cannot be cooked and is eaten cold

**Thali** – a plate made of steel. Also a complete meal comprising small dishes of vegetable curries, **chapattis** or **pooris**, rice, pickles, **dhal** or **khadi** and **farsan**. Equivalent in status to the Sunday roast

**Thamta** – green **poppadum** made with moong flour and **hing**

**Thums Up** – an Indian soft drink similar to Coca Cola

**Tilak** – mark, usually on the forehead, either for style or as part of a religious ritual

**Tiffin** – lunch, often packed in containers; can be as elaborate as a **thali**

**Undhiyu** – means upside-down; a method of cooking in which spiced vegetables are buried underground and allowed to cook slowly

**Vada** – popular fried breakfast snack made of urad **dhal,** with a crispy exterior and softer interior; served with coconut and vegetable chutney

**Vagar** – a mix of fried mustard seeds, **hing,** chillis, garlic and ginger, the beginning of many Gujarati curries. Can also be added at the end, as with **khadi** and **dhal**

**Viman** – aeroplane

**Vishnu** – second god of the Hindu triumvirate, responsible for the creation and upkeep of the world

**Wallah** – person associated with a specific business or place, eg rickshaw-wallah; Delhi-wallah